BACTERIA IN ENVIRONMENTAL BIOTECHNOLOGY: THE MALAYSIAN CASE STUDY- ANALYSIS, WASTE UTILIZATION AND WASTEWATER REMEDIATION

BACTERIOLOGY RESEARCH DEVELOPMENTS

BACTERIA IN ENVIRONMENTAL BIOTECHNOLOGY: THE MALAYSIAN CASE STUDY-ANALYSIS, WASTE UTILIZATION AND WASTEWATER REMEDIATION

WAN AZLINA AHMAD
ZAINOHA ZAKARIA
AND
ZAINUL AKMAR ZAKARIAB
EDITORS

Nova Science Publishers, Inc.
New York

NOTICE TO THE READER

The Publisher has taken reasonable care in the preparation of this book, but makes no expressed or implied warranty of any kind and assumes no responsibility for any errors or omissions. No liability is assumed for incidental or consequential damages in connection with or arising out of information contained in this book. The Publisher shall not be liable for any special, consequential, or exemplary damages resulting, in whole or in part, from the readers' use of, or reliance upon, this material.

Independent verification should be sought for any data, advice or recommendations contained in this book. In addition, no responsibility is assumed by the publisher for any injury and/or damage to persons or property arising from any methods, products, instructions, ideas or otherwise contained in this publication.

This publication is designed to provide accurate and authoritative information with regard to the subject matter covered herein. It is sold with the clear understanding that the Publisher is not engaged in rendering legal or any other professional services. If legal or any other expert assistance is required, the services of a competent person should be sought. FROM A DECLARATION OF PARTICIPANTS JOINTLY ADOPTED BY A COMMITTEE OF THE AMERICAN BAR ASSOCIATION AND A COMMITTEE OF PUBLISHERS.

Additional color graphics may be available in the e-book version of this book.

LIBRARY OF CONGRESS CATALOGING-IN-PUBLICATION DATA
Bacteria in environmental biotechnology : the Malaysian case study-analysis,
waste utilization and wastewater remediation / editors, Wan Azlina Ahmad,
Zainoha Zakaria and Zainul Akmar Zakariab.
p. cm.
Includes index.
ISBN 978-1-61728-350-5 (softcover)
1. Bioremediation. 2. Microbial biotechnology. I. Ahmad, Wan Azlina. II.
Zakaria, Zainoha. III. Zakariab, Zainul Akmar.
TD192.5.B33 2009
628.5--dc22
2010025432

Published by Nova Science Publishers, Inc. ✤ *New York*

CONTENTS

PREFACE

Environmental biotechnology encompasses a wide field of science and engineering. In a nutshell, it revolves around the use of microorganisms in a well-defined process to produce something valuable to mankind. Real-time practitioners, academicians, researchers and students from different backgrounds such as chemistry, biochemistry, chemical engineering, bioprocess engineering, environmental scientists and engineers, microbiologist, statisticians and sometimes mechanical engineers, would happily stake a claim that they would somewhat contribute towards the advancement of knowledge in this exciting field.

During the last 15 or 20 years, Malaysia has put a great emphasis on the importance of biotechnology in driving the future of the country's economy and wealth. Numerous funding and research grants have been made available to the academia, researchers and biotechnologists to pursue their interests, whether in the laboratory or at the pilot-scale. The government, via the Ministry of Science, Technology and Innovation (MOSTI), always encouraged a close collaboration between researchers and industry as to ensure all research outputs can be benefited as quickly and as usefully as possible to the intended beneficiaries.

We believe that this book, written as a case study approach, will provide an insight into important aspects of Environmental Biotechnology. The content includes applications of bacteria for the removal of toxic and precious metals from solution, degradation of phenol and production of protein liquor from solid waste obtained from the fisheries industry. There are also chapters (8 and 9) that focus solely on the interactions between metals and bacteria. Even though the chapters presented in this book described work carried out at lab-scale, the experiments were designed for applications in the industry. This is evident from the direct involvements by various industries such as electroplating enterprise, oil processing facility, Brackishwater Aquaculture Research Center and PERMINT Minerals.

We are highly indebted to the contributors for their enthusiastic support and cooperation in preparing this book. We are also grateful to the Ministry of Science, Technology and Innovation, Malaysia (MOSTI) for the financial support. This book might not serve everyone in the area of Environmental Biotechnology; however, we envisage that this book would interest academicians, practitioners, researchers, entrepreneurs, policymakers, graduate students and anyone keen in applying bacteria in various processes.

In: Bacteria in Environmental Biotechnology   ISBN 978-1-61728-350-5
Editor: W. A. Ahmad, et al.   © 2011 Nova Science Publishers, Inc.

Chapter 1

BACTERIAL REDUCTION OF Cr(VI) - CONTAINING ELECTROPLATING WASTEWATER UTILIZING AGRICULTURAL WASTES

Wan Azlina Ahmad, Salmijah Surif and Zainul Akmar Zakaria

ABSTRACT

Acinetobacter haemolyticus, a Gram-negative aerobic locally isolated bacterium, immobilized on wood husk, showed the ability to detoxify Cr(VI) to Cr(III). Wood husk, a natural cellulose-based support material, packed in an upward-flow column was used as support material for bacterial attachment. Around 97% of the Cr(VI) in wastewater containing 15 mg L^{-1} of Cr(VI) was reduced when liquid pineapple wastewater (LPW) was used as nutrient. Substitution of the LPW with brown sugar resulted in a much higher Cr(VI) reduction capacity for the bacteria, with 99.8 to 100% of the initial 237 to 320 mg L^{-1} of Cr(VI) reduced. This remarkable Cr(VI) removal capacity was largely assisted by the abiotic Cr(VI) reduction by brown sugar used. The column Cr(VI) reduction capacity increases with column length, indicating the importance of column design to ensure process efficiency. The high percentage conversion of Cr(VI) to Cr(III) suggests the feasibility of using a bacterial system as an alternative treatment for Cr(VI) contamination in the aqueous system. The use of 0.1% (v/v) formaldehyde as a disinfecting agent inhibited growth of bacteria present in the final wastewater discharge. This finding is important in view of the ethical code regarding possible introduction of exogenous bacterial species into the environment.

INTRODUCTION

Chemical reduction followed by precipitation is the most common technique used in the industry to remove Cr(VI) (Cushnie, 1985). However, this technique has its own serious disadvantages, such as the possibility of chemical spillage and the high cost of treatment chemicals, while the large generation of sludge leads to disposal problems. This prompts the need to look into safer and cheaper alternatives to carry out the Cr(VI) reduction process such as biological processes. Numerous reports have demonstrated the feasibility of using bacterial processes for the treatment of Cr(VI)-containing industrial wastewaters by use of either a pure culture or a bacterial consortium (Romanenko et al. 1976; Bopp and Ehrlich, 1988). Bacteria of various genera have been used including *Achromobacter, Aeromonas, Agrobacterium, Bacillus, Desulfovibrio, Enterobacter* and *Pseudomonas* (Wang, 2000). These bacteria showed different Cr(VI) reducing capacity depending on factors such as availability of organic compounds as electron donor, dissolved oxygen, Cr(VI) concentration, pH, redox potential, temperature, presence of other electron acceptors and inhibition effects by metallic or phenolic compounds (Wang, 2000; Ishibashi et al., 1990). In this study, wood husk was chosen as the column support material for bacterial attachment because it is a natural source for cellulose that is known for its bacterial attachment property, and it is inexpensive and stable. Another point to note is that the glucose-containing pineapple waste is readily consumed by *Acinetobacter haemolyticus*, and so is an effective substitute for expensive growth medium such as NB (Ivy, 2005). One example of a bioremediation process that was short lived due to its requirement for a high cost nutrient was the bacterial-based metal removal system developed by Advanced Mineral Technologies, Inc. in Colorado that used *Bacillus sp.* as the biosorbent (Volesky, 1990).

Bacterial reduction of Cr(VI) can be considered as a mechanism of resistance to Cr(VI). Cr(VI) is a strong oxidizing agent that can easily penetrate the cell membrane of prokaryotic cells such as bacteria. Cr(VI) uptake is carried out by the sulfate transport pathway; hence, it is competitively inhibited by sulfate (Ohtake et al., 1987). However, the role of sulfate as inhibitor for Cr(VI) uptake is more pronounced in anaerobic cells (Komori et al., 1989) compared to aerobic cells (Wang, 2000). The ability of Cr(VI) anions to overcome the permeability barrier of a prokaryotic cell can be attributed to the chemical similarity between CrO_4^{2-} and SO_4^{2-} ions (Mabbettt and Macaskie, 2001). Bacterial resistance to Cr(VI) was reported to be plasmid-determined. Cr(VI) resistance was also related to the decrease in Cr(VI) accumulation in resistant cells compared with the sensitive cells (Cervantes, 1991). The aerobic Cr(VI) reduction is normally associated with a soluble protein fraction utilizing NADH or NADPH as electron donor (Camargo et al., 2003), whereas in anaerobic condition, Cr(VI) can act as the terminal electron acceptor through membrane-bound reductase activity, which was reported in *Pseudomonas aeruginosa*, *Pseudomonas fluorescens* and *Enterobacter cloacae* by Wang and Xiao (1995). Aerobic reduction is considered to be a detoxification mechanism where normally the reduction of Cr(VI) by the soluble protein fraction takes place either internal or external to the plasma membrane. In the anaerobic respiration of *Enterobacter cloacae* HO1, possible involvement of the respiratory chain in the transfer of reducing equivalents to anionic Cr(VI) compounds through cytochrome c was implicated (Shen and Wang, 1993). Anaerobic reduction of Cr(VI) by six strains of Cr-resistant *Pseudomonads* was also reported. However, it was postulated that energy generated in the anaerobic respiration process is insufficient to sustain cell growth because fermentable organic compounds generated is utilized for cell metabolism (Mclean and Beveridge, 2001). Besides that, some of the bacteria were able to reduce Cr(VI) either aerobically or anaerobically. *Pseudomonas ambigua* G-1 and *Pseudomonas putida* PRS2000 were reported to reduce Cr(VI) in both conditions with higher reduction rates under aerobic conditions. However, opposite trend was observed for *Enterobacter coli* ATCC 33456 where Cr(VI) reduction proceeded at higher rate anaerobically.

This work reports on the reduction of Cr(VI) in electroplating wastewater using wood husk immobilized bacterial bioiflm. Two kinds of agricultural wastes were used as nutrient for the bacteria, namely, the liquid pineapple waste and brown sugar.

BIOREACTOR AND RAW MATERIALS

The laboratory-scale bioreactor consist of a glass column with inner diameter (I.D.) 8.0 cm, outer diameter (O.D.) 8.70 cm and height 100 cm was used. Inlet and outlet points were set at 2 cm from the bottom and top of column, respectively. Teflon tubing with I.D of 2.0 mm and O.D. of 4.0 mm was fitted to the inlet and outlet points, respectively. The teflon tubes were sterilized by soaking in 100% ethanol before use. Inert stones were packed to 75 cm^3 at the bottom of the column to ensure good flow distribution inside the column and to retain the column content. Following this, wood husk was packed into the column to a volume of 825 cm^3. This volume is considered as the working volume of the column. Inert stone was then packed on top of the working volume for 50 cm^3. A headspace of around 30 cm^3 was allowed in the column. The total volume of the column is, therefore, 1000 cm^3. A modified procedure from Von Canstein et al. (1999) was used during the immobilization of *Acinetobacter haemolyticus* cells onto wood husk packed in the column. The column was first rinsed with deionised water to prevent clogging by large particulate substances on the support material and to allow the wood husk surface material to acquire necessary charge for bacterial attachment. Then, 1 L of the *Acinetobacter haemolyticus* culture (grown for 24 h in NB) was pumped using the same flow rate as the rinsing step. The wastewater collected was recycled back into the column and pumped continuously for 6 h to allow bacterial attachment. A mixture of 20% (v/v) NB in 1 L pineapple waste (final pH of mixture 7.00) was pumped into the column using the same flow rate as *Acinetobacter haemolyticus* cells for 24 h to ensure initial formation of biofilm by the attached bacteria.

Acinetobacter haemolyticus was used as the primary strain inoculated inside the bioreactor. It was isolated from the Cr(VI)-containing wastewater from a batek (textile-related) manufacturing premise in Kota Bharu, Kelantan, Malaysia. *Acinetobacter haemolyticus* was cultivated in NB (8 g L^{-1}, Merck) at 200 rpm and 30 °C (Certomat, B. Braun). It was identified via the 16S rRNA gene sequencing analysis carried out by First BASE Laboratories Sdn. Bhd., Malaysia where a 99.5% similarity with *Acinetobacter haemolyticus* (AY586400 and X81662) was obtained from the nucleotide sequence of 597 bp. The nucleotide suquence was deposited to GenBank, where it was given the accession number EF369508.

Brown sugar used was obtained from local sundry shops. In this chapter, unsterilized stock solution of brown sugar (200 g L^{-1} in deionized water) was used. Results from the analysis on brown sugar are as follows: total sugar content of 154.2 ± 10.9 g L^{-1}, total nitrogen at 383.00 ± 12.73 g L^{-1}, ammonia at 0.4645 ± 0.0148 and nitrate at 1.696 ± 0.055 g L^{-1}, elemental compositions in mg L^{-1}; Pb (0.03), Cu (0.13), Zn (2.94), As (0.03), Fe (8.26), Hg (not detected), Ni (0.26), Cd (0.01) and Cr (13.46).

Table 1.1. Survival of indigenous microorganisms in LPW after treatment with 1 to 5% (v/v) ethanol

Pre-treatment of LPW	(*CFU mL^{-1})
1% (v/v) ethanol	1×10^5
3% (v/v) ethanol	3×10^4
5% (v/v) ethanol	0

* CFU – colony forming unit; counted based on two distinct colonies formed on NA plate, LPW without any treatment acted as control.

Table 1.2. Profile of metal concentrations in pre- and post-treated electroplating wastewater (EW)*

Element	Pre-treated EW, mg L^{-1}	Post-treated EW, mg L^{-1}	Standard B, mg L^{-1}
Pb	1.97 ± 0.43	1.34 ± 0.22	0.50
As	0.29 ± 0.13	0.29 ± 0.07	0.10
Hg	0.02 ± 0.01	0.03 ± 0.02	0.05
Cu	0.63 ± 0.11	0.66 ± 0.07	1.00
Fe	1.49 ± 0.18	1.48 ± 0.07	5.00
Ni	4.76 ± 1.67	4.62 ± 0.72	1.00
Cd	0.08 ± 0.01	0.06 ± 0.02	0.02
Cr	28.77 ± 2.38	0.18 ± 0.49	0.05

*values shown are means of triplicate sample; Standard B – permissible discharge limit for industrial wastewater outside the catchment area in Malaysia.

Rubber wood sawdust (RWS) used in this study was collected from the compound of a wood finishing factory in Skudai, Malaysia. Sawdust collected originated from the rubber wood treated with the chromated copper arsenate (CCA). The specific surface area was determined using the Surface Area Analyzer ASAP 2010 (Micromeritics, USA). The values for specific surface areas obtained by BET, Langmuir and Single Point (at P/ Po = 0.2002) methods were 3.0025, 5.8345 and 1.9806 m^{2}g^{-1}, respectively, while the average pore diameter was 694.03 nm. In this study, the RWS was used without any other physical or chemical treatment, hence the term URWS (untreated rubber wood sawdust).

Liquid pineapple waste was used as the energy source for bacteria. It was obtained from one pineapple-processing premise in Tampoi, Johor. The liquid pineapple waste (LPW) normally appears as yellowish green, slightly turbid, pH – 3.19 to 4.17 ± 0.28, 33.9 °C ± 1.61, sulphate – 58.2 ± 1.41 mg L^{-1} and microbiological count – four colonies isolated. From the ICP–MS analysis, concentrations of Pb, As, Hg, Cu and Cr exceed the permitted level. Sugar content was as follows: glucose 4.95 g L^{-1} and fructose 4.49 g L^{-1}. Sucrose content was relatively low in comparison with the glucose and fructose, and hence was not readily detected. The reduction of the glucose and fructose concentrations to the undetectable levels after three days of storage at both room temperature and at 4 °C was due to the consumption by indigenous bacteria from LPW as supported by Tseng and Bielefeldt (2002). The effectiveness of LPW treatment using different concentrations of ethanol is shown in Table 1.1. From the results obtained, 5% (v/v) ethanol managed to kill all the indigenous microorganisms present in the LPW, hence its selection as method of choice for preserving the LPW. However after two days of treatment, the LPW showed signs of microorganisms' growth when left at room temperature that can be attributed to the rich sugar content of the LPW itself. The electroplating wastewater was obtained from the rinse-bath tank of a local electroplating company in Pasir Gudang, Johor. The electroplating wastewater showed the following characteristics: colour – yellow to dark orange, turbidity – clear, pH – between 2.30 to 2.70 ± 0.05, temperature - 30.7 °C ± 3.39, sulphate - 4.45 ± 3.32 mg L^{-1}. Microbiological count did not yield any colonies. Profile for the heavy metals content of the raw electroplating wastewater is shown in Table 1.2.

OPERATION OF THE BIOREACTOR – LPW AS NUTRIENT

The experimental setup for the Cr(VI) reduction system consists of a holding tank, peristaltic pump, column (bioreactor), precipitation tank and disinfection tank. Solution from the holding tank consisting of 15 mg L^{-1} Cr(VI) from electroplating and pineapple wastewaters was first adjusted to pH 7.0 using 15% (v/v) NaOH solution. The solution was then pumped into the *A. haemolyticus*-immobilized column at 3.0 mL min^{-1} until the Cr(VI) concentration in the effluent fraction was more than 0.5 mg L^{-1}. At this point, a decrease in the population of the Cr(VI)–reducing *Acinetobacter haemolyticus* was expected due to Cr(VI) toxicity. The column was then regenerated using NB followed by pineapple waste. Then, 200 mL of fresh *Acinetobacter haemolyticus* culture, grown for 24 h in NB, was introduced before the column was left idle for three days to allow biofilm formation (Von Canstein et al. 2001). Then, Cr(VI) reduction was continued for 30 days when the influent flow rate was varied between 3.0 to 8.0 mL min^{-1}. The following parameters were periodically measured: Cr(VI) and total Cr concentrations, heavy metals, pH, microbiological count and dissolved oxygen (DO).

Bacterial reduction of Cr(VI) in simulated effluent and electroplating wastewater (EW) was carried out for 24 h using *A. haemolyticus* in LPW supplemented with NB. Figure 1.1 shows profiles for bacterial growth (OD_{600}) and Cr(VI) reduction in 50 mg L^{-1} simulated solution and real EW.

Figure 1.1. shows an inversely proportional relationship of *A. haemolyticus* growth with amount of Cr(VI) reduced. Rapid reduction of Cr(VI) was observed in the exponential growth phase of the bacteria i.e., 4 to 12 h. A higher Cr(VI) reduction was observed in simulated solution (99.27%) compared to in EW (95.35%). The consumption of glucose resulted in increase biomass that ultimately promotes Cr(VI) reduction. A similar finding was reported by Tseng and Bielefeldt (2002), where carbon availability was cited as the most critical factor limiting chromium biotransformation. Also, sugar addition had the greatest effect on enhancing Cr(VI) removal. Glucose as a major constituent in the LPW serves as electron donor and Cr(VI) serves as terminal electron acceptors along with oxygen (Wang and Xiao, 1995).

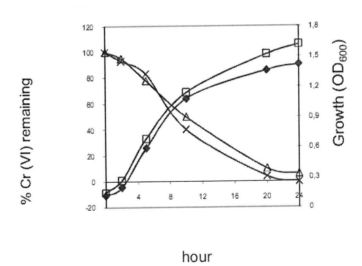

hour

Figure 1.1. Growth and reduction of Cr(VI) by *A. haemolyticus*; (□) Growth in LPW - NB (3 : 2) and 50 mg L-^{1} simulated Cr(VI) solution, (◆) Growth in LPW - NB (3 : 2) and EW, (x)% Cr(VI) remaining in LPW – NB (3 : 2) and 50 mg L^{-1} simulated Cr(VI) solution, (●)% Cr(VI) remaining in LPW - NB (3 : 2) and EW.

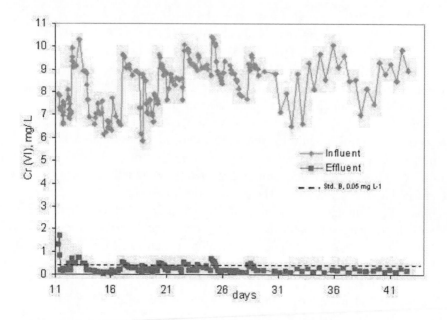

Figure 1.2. Profile for bioremediation of Cr(VI) from electroplating wastewater by wood- husk-immobilized *Acinetobacter haemolyticus* in a column system..

Rapid reduction of Cr(VI) at exponential phase of growth indicated that the rate of Cr(VI) reduction was strongly dependent on the bacterial cell density. Lower Cr(VI) reduction by *A. haemolyticus* was observed for EW compared to the simulated Cr(VI) solution. The existence of ions such as sulphate may hinder the bioreduction of Cr(VI), as it competes for the reducing capacity generated by NADH in the bacterial cell. In the presence of high concentration of sulphate, Cr(VI) reduction can be inhibited as CrO_4^{2-} and SO_4^{2-} are known to be transported by the same carrier proteins due to chemical similarities (Ganguli and Tripathi, 1999). Initial influent Cr(VI) concentration was 8.37 mg L^{-1} with Cr(VI) reduction around 55.33% (Figure 1.2).

Lowering of influent Cr(VI) concentration did not result in increased Cr(VI) reduction. More than 95% of Cr(VI) reduction was achieved after three days of column operation. However, the inability to achieve effluent Cr(VI) concentration below the discharge limit (Std. B, 0.05 mg L^{-1}) prompted the column operation to be stopped to allow a regeneration step. After regeneration, the effect of influent flow rate and column retention time on Cr(VI) reduction was investigated. Cr(VI) reduction was not affected up to influent flow rate of 8.0 mL min^{-1} at Cr(VI) concentration of 7.37 to 8.44 mg L^{-1} when more than 99% Cr(VI) was reduced. Variation of influent flow rate

(3.0 to 8.0 mL min^{-1}) corresponds to R_t of 1.72 to 4.58 h (volume of column – 825 cm^3). A flow rate of 8.0 mL min^{-1} and Cr(VI) concentration less than 15 mg L^{-1} was used throughout the study. Around 93.50 to 96.93% of influent Cr(VI) was converted to Cr(III). AAS analysis of the influent and effluent fractions shows that a high percentage of the total Cr was recovered in the effluent portion with average value of 83.77 ± 5.48%. Since the column operation was carried out under non-sterile conditions, *Acinetobacter haemolyticus* biofilm formed may be subjected to colonization by ubiquitous Cr(VI) resistant bacteria. At this time, it can be stated that the invading microorganisms were beginning to have a role in the biofilm as evident from its good survival ability. This could explain the high Cr(VI) reduction capacity of cells. During biofilm development, portions of biofilm peel away from the surface and are entrained in the fluid flow. Detachment is a process of continuous biofilm removal and is highly dependent on hydrodynamic conditions such as flow rate and toxicity. The presence of toxic substances or the limitations on by–product diffusion from the biofilm further aggravate the situation and would lead to death or lysis of the bacteria (Annachatre and Bhamidimarri, 1992). Most studies on biological reduction of Cr(VI) have been conducted in batch reactors using pure cultures (Wang and Xiao, 1995; Shakoori et al., 2000; Megharaj et al., 2003). It is only recently that continuous–flow and fixed–film bioreactors were used for biological reduction of Cr(VI) (Chirwa and Wang, 1997; Shen and Wang, 1995; Krishna and Philip, 2005). This study consists of four main phases i.e., optimization of influent Cr(VI) concentration, column regeneration, variation in influent flow rate and sustainability of Cr(VI) reduction in continuous operation. A regeneration step was necessary to counter the expected decrease of bacterial population in column from Cr(VI) toxicity during optimization of influent Cr(VI) concentration. The ability of *Acinetobacter haemolyticus* to use pineapple waste as carbon source has been reported. *Acinetobacter haemolyticus* showed good growth in 15% v/v pineapple waste, with glucose identified as the main sugar component utilized by the bacteria compared to sucrose and fructose. Around 80% of 2.97 g glucose L^{-1} was consumed by *Acinetobacter haemolyticus*.

OPERATION OF THE BIOREACTOR – BROWN SUGAR AS NUTRIENT

The experimental setup for the Cr(VI) reduction system consists of a holding tank, peristaltic pump, air pump, column (bioreactor) and precipitation tank, shown in Figure 1.3.

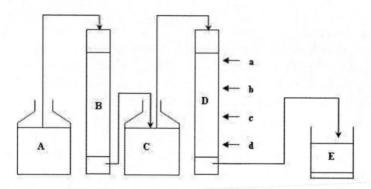

Figure 1.3. Cr(VI) solution was mixed with brown sugar in a holding tank (A) before passing through URWS-packed glass column (B), unadsorped Cr(VI) was collected in (C) prior to reduction process by immobilized bacteria on URWS in (D), Cr(III) was then collected in (E) for precipitation step; glass columns with inner diameter (i.d.) of 8.0 cm, outer diameter (o.d.) of 8.70 cm and 150 cm height was used; teflon tubing - I.D. of 2.0 mm and O.D. of 4.0 mm; a, b, c, d – sampling points.

After the initial column immobilization by the bacteria, 3 L solution of 1 g L^{-1} brown sugar was pumped into the column for 48 h to allow initial biofilm formation by the attached bacteria. Then, the wastewater mixture present in the holding tank (*A*) consisting of 236.5 to 320.4 mg L^{-1} of Cr(VI) and 1 g L^{-1} brown sugar was transferred into the URWS-packed glass column (*B*). Raw tap water was used as bulk solution. Wastewater mixture containing the unadsorped Cr(VI) was collected in a receiving vessel (*C*), sparged with air prior to transferring into the URWS-immobilized packed column (*D*) for bioreduction at a flow rate of 3.0 - 8.0 mL min $^{-1}$. The resulting solution was then collected in a vessel (*E*) for precipitation and adsorption by activated carbon. The combination of URWS and URWS-immobilized *A. haemolyticus* displayed a very high percentage of Cr(VI) removal capacity (Figure 1.4).

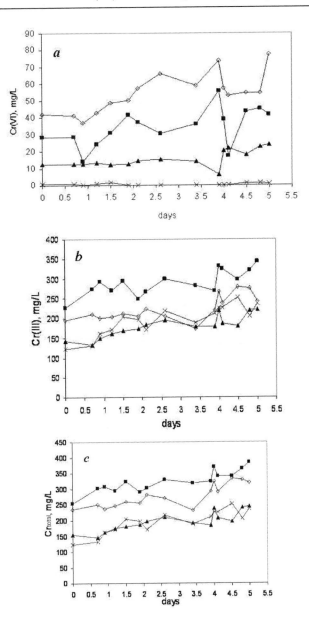

Figure 1.4. Cr(VI) removal profile by the combination of URWS and URWS-immobilized *A. haemolyticus*, a – Cr(VI), b – Cr(III), c – total chromium; Legend: ◇ - URWS inlet, ■ – URWS outlet, ▲ – URWS-*A. haemolyticus* inlet, x – URWS-*A. haemolyticus* outlet.

Spontaneous reduction of Cr(VI) by 1 g L^{-1} brown sugar used, probably carried out by glucose and other reducing sugars present in the brown sugar, also helped lowered Cr(VI) toxicity towards *A. haemolyticus*. This is evident from the Cr(VI) and the total Cr profiles shown in Figs 1.4a and 1.4c, respectively. With reference to the URWS inlet profiles (legend ◇), from the initial 237 to 320 mg L^{-1} Cr(VI) (determined as total Cr by AAS, Figure 1.5c) mixed with brown sugar and tap water in the holding tank (*A*), around 75 to 83% of Cr(VI) were spontaneuosly reduced, leaving around 40 to 80 mg L^{-1} Cr(VI) (Figure 1.4a) to be treated using URWS and URWS-immobilized *A. haemolyticus*.

The difference between total chromium and Cr(VI) values was taken as Cr(III), as shown in Figure 1.4b. The ability of the system to remove Cr(VI) was substantially higher than reported previously (Chen and Gu, 2005). URWS showed the ability to remove 25 to 50% of Cr(VI), as shown from the difference between Cr(VI) concentrations at the URWS inlet (40 to 80 mg L^{-1}) and outlet (30 to 40 mg L^{-1}) fractions, as shown in Figure 1.4a. This was due to the negligible volume of micropores available (based on average pore diamater of 694 nm) and the low surface area of the URWS as described earlier. Cr(VI) can be removed from the aqueous solution by nonliving biomass such as URWS via two mechanisms (Park and Park, 2006). The first mechanism involves direct reduction of Cr(VI) to Cr(III) in the aqueous phase by contact with the electron-donor groups on the biomass having lower reduction potential values than + 1.3 V, i.e., that of Cr(VI) (Katz and Salem, 1994). It was established that when Cr(VI) comes into contact with organic substances or reducing agents in an acidic medium, the Cr(VI) is easily or spontaneously reduced to the Cr(III) (Lytle et al., 1998; Gardea-Torresdey et al., 2000). The second mechanism consists of three steps starting with the binding of anionic Cr(VI) ion species to the positively charged groups present on the biomass surface. Then Cr(VI) reduction to Cr(III) takes place by the adjacent electron-donor groups. Finally, Cr(III) ions will be released into the aqueous phase due to electronic repulsion between the positively charged groups and the Cr(III) ions, or the complexation of the Cr(III) with adjacent groups capable of Cr-binding such as oxygen. Oxygen is an important heteroatom for Cr(VI) adsorption, which commonly occurs in the form of carboxylic acid, phenolic hydroxyl and quinone carbonyl groups (Liu et al., 2007). If there are a small number of electron-donor groups in the biomass or protons in the aqueous phase, the chromium bound on the biomass can remain in the hexavalent state (Mohan and Pitmann Jr., 2006). At any given time, these two mechanisms would occur concurrently depending on the parameters involved such as pH, temperature, biomass concentration, functional groups present on the biomass and Cr(VI) concentration (Park and Park, 2006). Hence, it is rather inappropriate to address the mechanism occurring during the contact between Cr(VI) and URWS simply as "adsorption" or "reduction" because both reactions occur at the same time. Therefore, the term "removal" or "removed" would be more suitable.

The remaining Cr(VI) not removed by URWS was collected in an aerated receiving vessel for further removal by the URWS-immobilized *A. haemolyticus*. This aeration step further enhances spontaneous reduction of Cr(VI), as evident from the difference between Cr(VI) concentrations in the URWS outlet (30 to 40 mg L^{-1}) and URWS-*A. haemolyticus* inlet (10 to 20 mg L^{-1}) as depicted in Figure 1.4a. Upon passing the Cr(VI) solution through the URWS-immobilized *A. haemolyticus*, a maximum of 1.6 mg L^{-1} of Cr(VI) was determined in the URWS-*A. haemolyticus* outlet (Figure 1.4a) indicating 92 to 100% reduction of Cr(VI) by the URWS-immobilized *A. haemolyticus*. In view of the initial Cr(VI) used, i.e., 237 to 320 mg L^{-1}, this transmits into a Cr(VI) removal efficiency of 99.8 to 100%. A significant amount of Cr(VI), i.e., 110 to 117 mg L^{-1}, was also retained by URWS as shown from the difference between total Cr measured in the URWS-*A. haemolyticus* outlet (120 to 210 mg L^{-1}) and the URWS inlet, i.e., 237 to 320 mg L^{-1}. One significant feature of Cr(VI) reduction by URWS-immobilized *A. haemolyticus* is the increase in Cr(VI) reduction capacity with column length. Sampling point a, which is nearest to the column inlet point, showed lowest Cr(VI) tolerance level, i.e., 20 mg L^{-1} before residual Cr(VI) exceeds the permitted discharge value of 0.05 mg L^{-1}. This was followed by point b (50 mg L^{-1}), point c (80 mg L^{-1}) and point d (125 mg L^{-1}). Knowledge on the lowest tolerance level for Cr(VI) in the inlet flow that will result in residual Cr(VI) exceeding 0.05 mg L^{-1} is important, as it will indirectly indicate the efficiency of the column operation. Even though the bacterial populations present at point a were expected to give highest Cr(VI) reduction as it receives the highest concentration of dissolved oxygen and nutrient, it should be noted that it also received the highest incoming Cr(VI) concentration. The results clearly show that Cr(VI) toxicity towards the bacterial cells supersede the influence of high dissolved oxygen and nutrient concentrations. This effect of Cr(VI) toxicity on Cr(VI) reduction by *A. haemolyticus* and other bacteria present in the column was also reflected by the highest tolerance level of incoming Cr(VI) shown by point d, which is the furthest sampling point relative to the column inlet point. As Cr(VI) species percolates through the length of the column (through points a, b and c), most of the Cr(VI) was reduced to the less toxic Cr(III). Therefore, it can be concluded that the higher Cr(VI) tolerance level at point d can be attributed to most of chromium species reaching point d were in the Cr(III) forms rather than the more toxic Cr(VI) forms.

CONCLUSION

The bioreactor packed with wood husk for the attachment of *Acinetobacter haemolyticus* effectively reduced Cr(VI) without the need to resupply fresh cells. Wood husk looks promising as support material for biofilm development, while minimizing operating cost due to its abundance. The use of indigenous microbes such as *Acinetobacter haemolyticus*, which was isolated from a Cr(VI) containing wastewater, provides a certain advantage and ensures durability under various operating conditions. Reduction of Cr(VI) by *Acinetobacter haemolyticus* was significantly influenced by influent Cr(VI) concentration. The ability of *Acinetobacter haemolyticus* to utilize liquid pineapple wastewater and brown sugar as a nutrient is an excellent example of the substitution of a cheap and readily available industrial waste in place of expensive growth medium and could be a significant factor in the commercial use of a process such this. The high percentage conversion of Cr(VI) to Cr(III) by the system suggests this may be an efficient and economical method for removing Cr(VI) from industrial wastewater. The column Cr(VI) reduction capacity increases with column length, indicating the importance of column design to ensure process efficiency. The high percentage conversion of Cr(VI) to Cr(III) suggests the feasibility of using a bacterial system as an alternative treatment for Cr(VI) contamination in the aqueous system.

ACKNOWLEDGMENTS

The authors acknowledge the contribution from the Ministry of Science, Technology and Innovation (MOSTI), Malaysia for funding of the project under the TechnoFund grant (TF0106B001). We are also thankful to Nordiana Nordin (characterization of brown sugar) and Ang Ivy (early LPW work)..

REFERENCES

Bopp, L.H. and Ehrlich, H.L. 1988. Cr(VI) resistance and reduction in *Pseudomonas fluorescens* Strain LB300. *Archives of Microbiology.* 150: 426-431.

Camargo, F.A.O., Bento, F.M., Okeke, B.C., Frankenberger, W.T. 2003. Chromate reduction by chromium-resistant bacteria isolated from soils contaminated with dichromate. *Journal of Environmental Quality.* 32: 1228-1233.

Cervantes, C. 1991. Bacterial interactions with chromate. Antonie van Leeuwenhoek. 59: 229-233.

Chen, Y., Gu, G. 2005. Preliminary studies on continuous chromium (VI) biological removal from wastewater by anaerobic-aerobic activated sludge process. *Bioresource Technology.* 96: 1713–1721.

Chirwa, E.M.N., Wang, Y.T. 1997. Hexavalent chromium reduction by *Bacillus sp.* in a packed-bed bioreactor. *Environmental Science and Technology.* 31: 1446 – 1451.

Cushnie, G.C. Jr. 1985. Electroplating Wastewater Pollution Control Technology, Noyes Publications. New Jersey.

Ganguli A., Tripathi A.K. 1999. Survival and chromate reducing ability of *Pseudomonas aeruginosa* in industrial effluents. *Letters in Applied Microbiology.* 28: 76-80

Gardea-Torresdey, J.L., Tiemann, K.J., Armendariz, V., Bess-Oberto, L., Chianelli, R.R., Rios, J., Parsons, J.G., and Gamez, G. 2000. Characterization of Cr(VI) binding and reduction to Cr(III) by the agricultural byproducts of *Avenamonida* (oat) biomass. *Journal of Hazardous Materials.* 80, 175–188.

Ishibashi, Y., Cervantes, C., Silver, S. 1990. Chromium reduction in *Pseudomonas putida. Applied and Environmental Microbiology.* 56: 2268-2270.

Ivy, A., 2005. Bioreduction of Chromium (VI) from Electroplating wastewater Using *Acinetobacter haemolyticus* Grown in Pineapple Waste. Universiti Teknologi Malaysia. B. Sc. Thesis.

Katz, S.A., Salem, H. 1994. *The biological and environmental chemistry of chromium.* VCH Publishers Inc., USA.

Komori, K., Wang, P.C., Toda, K., Ohtake, H. 1989. Factors affecting chromate reduction in *Enterobacter cloacae* Strain HO1. *Applied Microbiology and Biotechnology.* 31: 567-570.

Krishna, K.R., Philip, L. 2005. Bioremediation of Cr(VI) in contaminated soils. *Journal of Hazardous Materials.* 121: 109 – 117.

Liu, S.X., Chen, X., Chen, X.Y., Liu, Z.F., Wang, H.L. 2007. Activated carbon with excellent chromium (VI) adsorption performance prepared by acid–base surface modification. *Journal of Hazardous Materials.* 141: 315–319.

Lytle, C.M., Lytle, F.W., Yang, N., Qian, J-H., Hansen, D., Zayed, A., and Terry, N. 1998. Reduction of Cr(VI) to Cr(III) by wetland plants: potential for in situ heavy metal detoxification. *Environmental Science and Technology,* 32, 3087–3093.

Mabbett, A.N., Macaskie, L.E. 2001. A novel isolate of *Desulfovibrio* sp. with enhanced ability to reduce Cr(VI), *Biotechnology Letters.* 23: 683-687.

Madigan M.T., Martinko J.M., Parker J. 2001. *Brock: biology of microorganisms*, 9th ed, New York, Prentice-Hall Int'l, USA.

McLean, J., Beveridge, T.J. 2001. Cr(VI) reduction by a *Pseudomonad* isolated from a site contaminated with chromated copper arsenate. *Applied and Environmental Microbiology.* 67: 1076-1084.

Megharaj, M., Avudaiyanagam, S., Naidu, R. 2003. Toxicity of hexavalent chromium and its reduction by bacteria isolated from soil contaminated with tannery waste. *Current Microbiology.* 47: 51-54.

Mohan, D., Pittman Jr., P.U. (2006) Activated carbons and low cost adsorbents for remediation of tri- and hexavalent chromium from water. *Journal of Hazardous Materials,* B137: 762–811.

Nigam J.N. 1998. Single cell protein from pineapple cannery effluent. *World Journal of Microbiology and Biotechnology.* 14: 693-696.

Ohtake, H., Cervantes, C., Silver, S. 1987. Decreased Cr(VI) uptake in *Pseudomonas fluorescens* carrying a Cr(VI) resistance plasmid. *Journal of Bacteriology.* 169: 3853-3856.

Park, D., Park, J.M. 2006. Mechanisms of the removal of hexavalent chromium by biomaterials or biomaterial-based activated carbons. *Journal of Hazardous Materials,* B137: 1254–1257.

Romanenko, V.I., Kuznetsov, S.I., Korenkov, V.I. 1976. Method of biological purification of industrial effluents from chromates and bichromates, US Patent 3941691.

Shakoori, A.R., Makhdoom, M., Haq, R.U. 2000. Hexavalent chromium reduction by a di Cr(VI)-resistant gram-positive bacterium isolated from effluents of tanneries. *Applied Microbiology and Biotechnology.* 53: 348-351.

Shen, H., Wang, Y.T. 1993. Characterization of enzymatic reduction of hexavalent chromium by *Escherichia coli* ATCC 33456. *Applied and Environmental Microbiology.* 59: 3771-3777.

Shen, H., Wang, Y.T. 1995. Hexavalent chromium removal in two-stage bioreactor system, *Journal of Environmental Engineering.* 121: 798 – 804.

Tseng J.K., Bielefieldt A.R. 2002, Low temperature chromium (VI) biotransformation in soil with varying electron acceptors. *Journal of Environmental Quality.* 31,: 1831 – 1841.

Wang, Y.T. 2000. Microbial reduction of chromate in Environmental Microbe-Metal Interaction. D. Lovley (ed.) ASM Press. Washington D.C. USA. 225-235.

Wang, Y.T., Xiao, C. 1995. Factors affecting hexavalent chromium reduction in pure cultures of bacteria. *Water Research.* 29: 2467-2474.

Volesky, B. 1990. Removal and Recovery of Heavy Metals by Biosorption. In Biosorption of Heavy Metals. B. Volesky, (ed.) Boca Raton Press. Florida. USA.

Von Canstein, H., Li, Y., Wagner-Dobler, I. 2001. Long-Term Performance of Bioreactors Cleaning Mercury-Contaminated Wastewater and Their Response to Temperature and Mercury Stress and Mechanical Pertubation. *Biotechnology and Bioengineering.* 74: 212-219.

Von Canstein, H., Li, Y., Timmis, K.N., Deckwer, W-D., Wagner-Dobler, I. 1999. Removal of Mercury from Chloralkali Electrolysis Wastewater by a Mercury-Resistant *Pseudomonas putida* Strain. *Applied and Environmental Microbiology.* 65: 5279-5284.

Wang Y.T., Xiao, C. 1995, Factors affecting hexavalent chromium reduction in pure cultures of bacteria. *Water Research*, 29: 2467-2474.

In: Bacteria in Environmental Biotechnology   ISBN 978-1-61728-350-5
Editor: W. A. Ahmad et al.   © 2011 Nova Science Publishers, Inc.

Chapter 2

BIOSORPTION OF Cr(VI), Cu(II) AND Ni(II) FROM AQUEOUS SOLUTION BY LOCALLY ISOLATED BACTERIA

Siti Khairunnisa Yahya, Seet Seow Wei and Suzalina Kamaralarifin

ABSTRACT

The ability of a bacterial consortium consisting of *A. haemolyticus* and *E. coli* to remove Cr(VI), Cu(II) and Ni(II) ions from aqueous solution has been demonstrated. pH plays a significant role during the binding of metals by the bacteria with Q_{max} (maximum adsorption values) of 384.6 mg g^{-1} for Cu(II) at pH 5.0, 109.9 mg g^{-1} for Cr(VI) at pH 2.0 and 62.5 mg g^{-1} for Ni(II), at pH 6.0. These values were achieved after a contact time of 10 h, initial metal concentration of less than 400 mg L^{-1} and biomass dosages ranging from 0.01 - 0.8 g cell dry wt. L^{-1}. Pretreatment of the bacterial biomass using either NaOH and HCl managed to increase the metal uptake compared to the untreated biomass. The ability of the bacteria to utilize LPW as a nutrient is an excellent example of the substitution of a cheap and readily available industrial waste in place of expensive growth medium and could be a significant factor in the commercial use of a process such this.

INTRODUCTION

Contamination of the environment can arise from the discharge of wastewater containing heavy metals such as Cr(VI), Ni(II) and Cu(II), which originates from various process industries. These waste streams can cause adverse impact to the environment and also to humans (Li et al., 2007). The conventional method for treating heavy metals includes chemical precipitation, ion exchange, reverse osmosis and solvent extraction. However, incomplete metal removal, high chemical reagent and energy requirements, or the formation of secondary waste that requires careful disposal has made it important to search for a cost-effective treatment method that is capable of removing heavy metals from aqueous effluents (Gomez and Callao, 2006). Therefore, it is imperative to find alternative methods with similar efficiency but that are more economical. The use of biological materials such as plants and microorganisms offer a lot of advantages compared to the conventional techniques. Microorganisms such as bacteria, yeast, and algae are known for their natural ability to sequester, accumulate, reduce, adsorb and oxidize toxic pollutants (BTEX, heavy metals, recalcitrant organics) when exposed to them. This serves as a means of survival in these extreme environments. The Cr(VI) ion is a strong oxidant, which acts as carcinogens, mutagens, and teratogens in biological system due to high solubility in water, rapid permeability through biological membranes and subsequent interaction with intracellular proteins and nucleic acids (Thacker et al., 2007). The structural similarity of the soluble chromate anion with biologically important inorganic anions, such as sulphate and phosphate, is responsible for its ability to readily transverse cell membranes via the sulfate transport system and can be incorporated into cells (Daulton et al., 2007). The Cr(VI) species maybe in the forms of dichromate ($Cr_2O_7^-$), hydrochromate ($HCrO_4^-$), or chromate (CrO_4^{2-}). Copper is a transitional metal with three common oxidation states: Cu0 (metal), Cu^+ (cuprous ion) and Cu^{2+} (cupric ion). Cu(II) is the most commonly occurring species, which readily forms free hydrated ion in water. It prevails in the environment and is the most toxic form to living organisms among the three species. The toxic effects of Cu(II) to microorganisms may reduce its abundance, biomass composition, shift in species composition and decrease in diversity. Cu(II) can also inhibit the biological process in wastewater treatment, i.e., aerobic-activated sludge and anaerobic sludge digestion in which microorganisms play an important role. Nickel is an essential trace element, which serves as a co-factor for several enzymes such as those involved in the metabolism of molecular hydrogen, urea and methane (Han et al., 2006). Ni(II) is categorized as a toxic metal, which can last for a long time in nature as well as damaging normal physiological activity and endangering human life indirectly (Kotas and Stasicka, 2000). Nickel and its related compounds were found to be carcinogenic and hence can cause lung and nasal sinus cancers (Anjana et al., 2007). The presence of nickel in industrial wastewater is common because it is used in a large number of industries such as electroplating and battery manufacturing as well as the manufacturing of printed circuit boards.

BACTERIAL BIOMASS

The bacteria used in this chapter, *Acinetobacter haemolyticus* (*A. haemolyticus*) and *Escherichia coli* (*E. coli*) were previously isolated from a batek (textile-related) manufacturing premise in Kota Bharu, Kelantan, Malaysia. A short-term bacterial stock culture was prepared by streaking a loopful of cells onto nutrient agar (NA) plate. The plate was incubated for 24 h and can be used immediately or stored at 4 °C for a maximum of 14 days until further use. One loopful of cells was taken from the NA plate (20 g L^{-1}) and inoculated into Erlenmeyer flask (500 mL) containing 40 mL of NB (NB) medium under sterile conditions. The flask was shaken at 200 rpm at 30°C for 12 h. (B. Braun, Certomat®R). Three types of growth medium were used, namely the liquid pineapple waste (LPW), NB (8 g L^{-1}) and LPW supplemented with brown sugar. The LPW was obtained from Lee Pineapple Manufacturing Industry, Tampoi. Solid particles present in the LPW were removed by filtration and the supernatant was centrifuged at 4 °C and 7000 rpm (B.Braun, SIGMA 4K-15). Growth profiles of *A. haemolyticus*, *E.coli* and the mixtures of both bacteria were monitored in neutralized LPW, NB and neutralized LPW supplemented with brown sugar. The 10% (v/v) inoculum were grown in a series of 1 L flasks containing 90% of the medium and incubated at 30 °C, 200 rpm for 24 h. Each set was complimented with a bacterial cell-free control set. The following parameters were monitored during the bacterial growth; OD$_{600}$, pH and the total sugar content. The total sugar content was characterized using the phenol-sulphuric acid method (Mecozzi, 2005). In this method, glucose was used as the standard solution in the range of 0 to 16 mg L^{-1}. A volume of standard solution and samples (2 mL) was mixed with 2 mL of 5% (w/w) aqueous solution of phenol and 10 mL of concentrated sulphuric acid. The mixture was cooled to room temperature prior to measurement at OD$_{490}$.

The metabolically inactive bacterial cultures were prepared as follows: each of the active bacterial cultures (*A. haemolyticus*, *E. coli* and mixed bacteria) were inoculated into 100% (v/v) of neutralized LPW and shaken at 200 rpm at 30 °C (B.Braun, Certomat®R). The cells were centrifuged at early stationary phase at 7000 rpm and 4 °C for 5 mins (B.Braun, SIGMA 4K-15). The supernatant was discarded while the pellet was washed with sterilized deionised water. After washing, the cells were suspended in minimal volume of sterilized deionised water and autoclaved at 121 °C for 15 mins (Hirayama). After autoclaving, the inactivated biomass (100 mg) was subjected to either acid or alkaline treatment using 50 mL of 0.1 M HCl of 0.1 M NaOH, in 250 mL Erlenmeyer flask. The flask was agitated at 120 rpm for 45 mins. The biomass was centrifuged at 9000 rpm and 4 °C for 15 mins and washed with deionised water to remove excess acid. Finally, the pretreated biomass was resuspended in minimal volume of deionised water and stored in the refrigerator prior to use. The dry weight of the acid/alkali-treated biomass were determined where 10 mL of the bacterial cells suspension were filtered through a pre-weighed and dried cellulose acetate membrane filter (0.45 μm pore size, Whatman). The membrane filter was dried in an oven at 60 °C until constant weight was achieved.

The growth profiles of *A. haemolyticus*, *E. coli* and mixed bacteria in NB and LPW are shown in Figure 2.1.

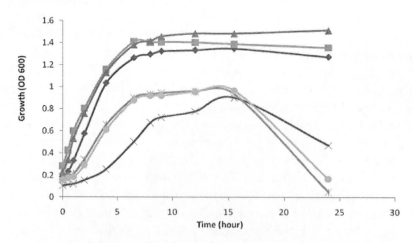

Figure 2.1. Growth profiles of *A. haemolyticus*, *E. coli* and mixed bacteria in NB and LPW; (◆)*A. haemolyticus* in NB, (■)*E. Coli* in NB, (▲)Mixed bacteria in NB, (✕) *A. haemolyticus* in LPW, (✱)*E. Coli* in LPW and (●) Mixed bacteria in LPW.

The initial pH of LPW obtained from pineapple industry was around 3.6 to 3.9. During the monitoring of the bacterial growth profiles, the pH was adjusted to 7, since it is the optimum growth pH for most bacteria. The growth profiles in Figure 2.1 also showed distinct growth phases of the bacteria, namely the lag, log, stationary and death phase. Higher bacterial growth ($OD_{600} > 1.2$) was observed in the NB medium compared to growth in 100% (v/v) LPW ($OD_{600} < 1.2$). This was due to the higher nutritional contents in the NB especially the carbon and protein contents, compared to LPW. It was also observed that a longer lag phase was seen in LPW compared to NB (Figure 2.1). Therefore, there would probably be a need to supplement the LPW with, for example, additional carbon in order to increase the biomass yield.

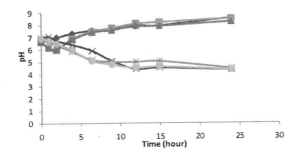

Figure 2.2. pH profile for bacterial growth in LPW and NB; (◆)A. haemolyticus in NB, (■)E. Coli in NB, (▲)Mixed bacteria in NB, (✖) A. haemolyticus in LPW, (✳)E. Coli in LPW and (●) Mixed bacteria in LPW.

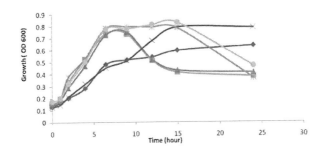

Figure 2.3. Growth profiles of A. haemolyticus, E. coli and mixed bacteria in LPW supplemented with 1 and 5% (v/v) of brown sugar (BS); (◆)A. haemolyticus in 1% BS, (■)E. Coli in 1% BS, (▲)Mixed bacteria in 1% BS, (✖) A. haemolyticus in 5% BS, (✳)E. Coli in 5% BS and (●) Mixed bacteria in 5% BS.

From the phenol-sulphuric acid method, the concentrations of sugar in LPW varies from 637.5 to 887.7 mg L^{-1}. The acidic pH of LPW ranging from 3.61 to 3.88 was mainly due to the citric acid and ascorbic acid contents from the pineapple fruit. A point to note is the decrease in sugar concentration with time due to acid hydrolysis and breakdown to hexose sugars by indigenous microorganisms present in the LPW. Therefore, in this study, the LPW was added with 5% (v/v) of ethanol as a means to inhibit the growth of indigenous microorganisms. Ethanol can act as the growth inhibitor for most bacteria, fungi and some viruses, as it has the ability to denature proteins and dissolve the lipid layers. It is also effective against most bacteria and fungi and many viruses. However, ethanol is ineffective against bacterial spores (Bueno et al., 2008). Figure 2.2 shows the pH profiles during bacterial growth in NB and LPW. In the LPW, the pH decreased with time from 7.0 ± 0.2 to between 4.14 to 4.81 (at the stationary phase). The pH decrease was caused from the formation of ethanol, acetic acid and lactic acid as a result of bacterial metabolic reaction (Madigan et al., 1997). While in NB, the pH increased with time from 7.0 ± 0.2 until between 7.88 to 8.54 at the stationary phase of growth. The observed pH increase in NB was due to the formation of basic substances during growth.

Figure 2.3 shows the growth of *A. haemolyticus*, *E. coli* and mixed bacteria bacterial consortium in LPW supplemented with different concentrations of brown sugar.

The addition of 1 and 5% (v/v) brown sugar did not seem to increase the biomass yield. One possible explanation is the rather extremely low carbon content present in 1 and 5% BS, hence not sufficient to play a role in inducing bacterial growth. The option of increasing the amount of brown sugar supplementation may be offset by its high pricing, even though the biomass yield may increase. Therefore, 100% (v/v) LPW was chosen as the culture medium for subsequent studies.

BIOSORPTION FROM SIMULATED EFFLUENT

The non-living mixed bacteria (5.0 mg, wet weight) was added into a series of 250 mL Erlenmeyer flasks and added with 1% (v/v) HNO$_3$ before being analyzed for metal concentration. During the adsorbent dosage study, 25 mL solutions containing of either 400 mg L^{-1} of Cr(VI) or Ni(II) were contacted for 10 h with varying wet weight biomass doses of 10, 20 and 30 mg. For the Cu(II) biosorption, 25 mL of 400 mg L^{-1} of Cu(II) in acetate buffer was mixed with 1 g of wood husk in a series of 250 mL Erlenmeyer flasks. The pH was adjusted to 5 prior to the addition of varying doses of biomass i.e., 10, 20 and 30 mg wet weight. The flasks were shaken at 100 rpm for 10 h at ambient temperature. Sample preparation prior to metal analysis was as described earlier. The metal solutions at pH 5 without the bacterial biomass and metal solutions without the wood husk acted as control. For the biomass pretreatment study, 25 mL of 400 mg L^{-1} Cr(VI) was mixed with 0.2 g L^{-1} of the HCl-treated biomass while the NaOH-treated biomass were added to 25 mL of 400 mg L^{-1} of Cu(II) and Ni(II) solutions, respectively. The mixtures were contacted for 10 h before metal analysis was carried out. Non-living bacterial biomass (5 mg) was added into a series of 250 mL Erlenmeyer flasks containing 25 mL of 25 to 400 mg L^{-1} of either Cu(II), Ni(II) or a mixture of both. The mixtures were then shaken at 100 rpm, for 24 h at room temperature. Samples were taken at the specified time intervals and centrifuged at 7000 rpm, 4 °C for 5 mins (B.Braun, SIGMA 4K-15). The supernatant was kept in the refrigerator and added with 1% (v/v) HNO$_3$ before being analyzed for metal concentration. The metal uptake, Q was calculated using the following equation 2.1. Control experiment consists of flasks containing 25 mL of either 25 mg L^{-1} Cr(VI) at pH 2, Cu(II) in acetate buffer at pH 5 or Ni(II) in PIPES buffer at pH 6. The mixtures were then shaken at 100 rpm, for 24 h at room temperature. Samples were taken at the specified time intervals and centrifuged at 7000 rpm, 4 °C for 5 mins (B.Braun, SIGMA 4K-15). The supernatant was kept in

$$Q(mg/g) = \frac{V(L) \times [C_i - C_f](mg/L)}{W(g)}$$
Equation (2.1)

With Q = metal uptake (mg of metal / g of dry weight biomass)
    V = volume of metal bearing solution (L)
    C_i = known initial metal concentration (mg L^{-1})
    C_f = final concentration of metal concentration
    W = amount of biomass added on dry basis (g)

The acetate buffer was prepared as follows: 14.8 mL of 0.1 M acetic acid were mixed with 35.2 mL of 0.1 M sodium acetate in 100 mL of deionized water. The pH was adjusted to 5 using either 0.1 M HCl or 0.1 M NaOH. For the preparation of 0.01 M PIPES buffer, 1.8925 g of piperazine - N, N'- bis (2 - ethanesulfonic acid) were dissolved in 500 mL of deionized water.

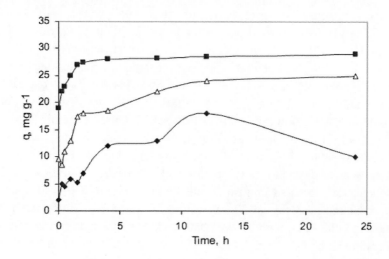

Figure 2.4. The biosorption profiles for mixed bacteria for Cr(VI) - (♦), Cu(II) – (△) and Ni(II) – (■).

The pH was then adjusted to 6. Stock solutions (1000 mg L^{-1}) of each metal were prepared by dissolving the following amounts of metal salts in 250 mL of deionised water; 0.7070 g of $K_2Cr_2O_7$, 0.6691 g of $CuCl_2.2H_2O$ and 1.0104 g of $NiCl_2$.

The mixed bacteria showed an immediate metal uptake capacity, a condition that may be attributed to the natural interactions between the metallic ions species with the various functional groups present on the bacterial cells surface (Figure 2.4).

The mixed bacteria showed a rapid Cu(II) uptake within the first 60 mins, followed by gradual increase until reaching equilibrium after 24 h of contact time. While for Cr(VI) and Ni(II), the metal uptake gradually increased and reaches equilibrium within 12 h. In this experiment, 10 h was chosen as the equilibrium time for all of the following biosorption experiments for the three metals because there was no significant difference in the uptake between 10 to 24 h. The rate of metal (Cr, Cu, Ni) uptake increases with increasing initial metal concentration with maximum metal uptake (Qe,max) of 36.2 mg g^{-1} for Cr(VI) and 84.4 mg g^{-1} for Cu(II) (Figure 2.4). These values were much lower compared to the theoretical values (Qm) of 109.9 mg g^{-1} for Cr(VI) and 384.6 mg g^{-1} for Ni(II), indicating that the biosorption process may proceed at a higher initial metal concentrations, as the surface of the mixed bacteria has not yet reached full equilibrium with metallic ions in the solution (Table 2.1).

Table 2.1.The equilibrium constants for the biosorption of Cr(VI), Cu(II) and Ni(II) by mixed bacteria

Metal	Langmuir Model			Freundlich Model		
	Q_m (mg g^{-1})	b (L mg^{-1})	r^2	K_f (mg g^{-1})	1 / n	r^2
Cr(VI)	109.9	0.0129	0.981	3.4	0.6111	0.978
Cu(II)	384.6	0.0035	1	1.6	1.12	0.996
Ni(II)	62.5	0.00310	0.936	12.1	0.841	0.726

The regression coefficients (r^2) of both models for Cr(VI) and Cu(II) adsorption were greater than 0.97, indicating that both models adequately describe the experimental data from the Cr(VI) and Cu(II) biosorption experiments. The Langmuir adsorption isotherm model describes a monolayer sorption with a homogeneous distribution of sorption sites and sorption energies, without interactions between the sorbed molecules (Han et al., 2007). The Freundlich isotherm has been developed to describe the concentration changes as a function of adsorption. For Ni(II) adsorption capacity, the value for r^2 showed that the data fitted the Langmuir model better than the Freundlich, which indicates that the adsorption of Ni(II) occur as a monolayer on the surface of bacterial biomass. The biosorption capacity of the mixed bacteria for Ni(II) decreased with increasing biomass dosage with the highest uptake of 18.4 mg g^{-1} obtained at the lowest biomass concentration used i.e., 0.2 g cell dry wt. L^{-1}. At higher biomass concentrations, the bacterial biomass can exert a shell effect, protecting the active sites from being occupied by metal and thus resulting in the decrease of Ni(II) uptake. However, the Cr(VI) uptake increased with increasing biomass concentration with maximum uptake of 65.68 mg g^{-1} at 0.8 g cell dry wt. L^{-1}. This observation can be attributed to the increase of the adsorption surface area and the availability of free adsorption sites (Mungasavalli et al., 2007).

The biosorption of Cu(II) by the combination of wood husk and mixed bacteria decreased with increasing biomass dosage. Highest Cu(II) removal of 8.67 mg g^{-1} was achieved from the use of 10 mg cell dry wt. The combination of biomass and wood husk also showed higher Cu(II) uptake compared to the use of wood husk only (7.44 mg g^{-1}). Wood husk was used as the support material for the bacteria in the study because it is a natural source for cellulose material. Cellulose contains glucose group, which has the hydroxyl groups that easily substituted, provide a weakly basic and acidic ion exchange conditions that enhance the bacterial attachment. Cellulose is also a porous material, which gives high surface area for bacterial attachment (Mashitah et al., 2007).

The HCl-treated biomass showed a higher Cr(VI) uptake capacity compared to the untreated biomass with Cr(VI) percentage removal values of 22.67% and 14.03%, respectively. This was due to the elimination of some impurities and ions that may block the binding sites (Mungasavalli et al., 2007). The metal uptake increased as a result of acid hydrolysis that yields relatively pure amino sugar, which is more easily protonated at adsorption pH (pH 2). This condition is supported from the FESEM analysis of the treated and untreated biomass (Figure 2.5), where the biomass' surface appears rougher after acid treatment, indicating the removal of impurities.

Similar results were obtained for the Ni(II) uptake using the NaOH-treated biomass. The Ni(II) biosorption increased from 0.58% to 4% after the biomass was treated using NaOH. The alkaline pretreatment was carried out to convert the active binding sites from the H^+ to the Na^+ form. This substitution favors the biosorption of Ni(II) because it is much easier to exchange Ni(II) for Na^+ than H^+ due to the size of the ions. In addition, pretreatment with NaOH may result in the rupture of the biomass cell wall to form additional functional groups in terms of metal binding sites (Figure 2.6). Remaining alkalinity can cause hydrolysis of various metals. Thus, an improvement in biosorption capacity of biomass may appear. Another point to note is the possibility of autolytic enzymes causing putrefaction of biomass and the removal of lipids and proteins as well as polysaccharides that mask binding sites.

Figure 2.5. Electron micrographs of the mixed bacteria a) before and b) after treatment with 0.1 M HCl.

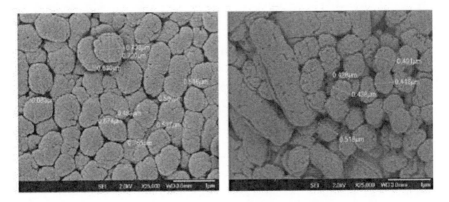

Figure 2.6. FESEM of (a) untreated and (b) 0.1 M NaOH-treated biomass.

BIOSORPTION FROM INDUSTRIAL WASTEWATER

Biosorption of Cr(VI) from Electroplating Wastewater (EW)

The HCl-pretreated biomass (5 mg) was added into 25 mL of EW at pH 2 in 250 mL Erlenmeyer flask. The mixture was then shaken at 100 rpm for 10 h. After 10 h, the solutions were taken out and centrifuged at 7000 rpm, 4 °C for 5 mins (B.Braun, SIGMA 4K-15). A new batch of HCl-pretreated biomass was added to the supernatant and shaken again for 10 h. The bacterial biomass was harvested and kept in the fridge until analyzed. The initial Cr(VI) concentration in the EW was determined at 10.56 mg L^{-1}, which was above the discharge limit (0.05 mg L^{-1}) (Han et al., 2007). Results obtained showed that the efficiency of Cr(VI) removal by mixed bacteria increased with increasing numbers of cycle. A total of 69.31% of Cr(VI) was removed from the EW after the first cycle. Upon the introduction of a new batch of mixed bacteria in the second cycle, the Cr(VI) removal percentage was increased to 89.48%. The same trend was observed for total chromium with the percentage removal increasing from 24.18% to 76.52%.

Biosorption Of Ni(II) and Cu(II) from Electrodeless Plating Nickel Wastewater

Two types of wastewater were, used namely the concentrated electrodeless nickel waste (CEN) and the rinse nickel waste (REN). Both samples (25 mL) were transferred into 250 mL Erlenmeyer flasks and the pH adjusted to 6. Bacterial suspensions of the NaOH-treated mixed bacterial biomass (0.2 g L^{-1}) were then added into the flasks followed by shaking at 100 rpm and 10 h. The initial and final concentrations of Ni(II) were analyzed using AAS. For the Cu(II) biosorption, 25 mL of the CEN and REN wastewaters were mixed with 1 g of wood husk in a series of 250 mL Erlenmeyer flasks. The pH was adjusted to 5 prior to the addition of varying doses of biomass, i.e., 10, 20 and 30 mg wet weight. The mixtures were shaken at 10 h prior to Cu analysis using FAAS. The Ni(II) concentrations from the concentrated electrodeless nickel effluent (CEN) and rinsed electrodeless plating effluents (REN) are 1864 mg L^{-1} and 17.3 mg L^{-1}, respectively. From this study, a total of 1% and 8.67% of Ni were removed from the CEN and REN waste by the NaOH-treated mixed bacteria. A higher percentage of Cu(II) was removed from the simulated effluent (9.52%) compared to the REN (4.92%) and CEN (0.31%). This could be due to the problematic nature of the wastewater as well as the waste produced by the industry during sampling time. As it is well known, the metal biosorption process strongly depends on the metal solution's chemistry and competing ions. The presence of considerable amounts of other metal ions in the real effluent may contribute to the lower percentage of Cu (II) removal, as they compete in occupying the binding sites (Tunali et al., 2003). The effectiveness of NaOH treatment in increasing the Cu(II) uptake efficiency of the biomass may be attributed to two pathways; the exposure of active metal-binding sites embedded in the cell wall or the chemical modifications of potential Cu-binding groups such as the sulphydryl and carboxyl compounds on the cell wall composition.

ELECTRON MICROSCOPY

The surface structures of untreated biomass and pretreated biomass were examined using FESEM. The pellets of the untreated and pretreated biomass were immersed in 2.5% (v/v) glutaraldehyde (1 - 2 h), 2% (v/v) osmium tetraoxide (1 h) followed by thorough washing using deionised water (Tunali et al., 2005). The bacterial pellet was then dehydrated using increasing concentrations of ethanol (25, 50, 70, 90, 100%) for 5 mins each. The bacterial pellet was dried overnight drying in a desiccator prior to viewing under the electron microscope. Figure 2.7 shows the attachment of bacteria on wood husk during the batch study, while the EDAX spectra (Table 2.2) corresponding to these electron dense areas exhibited pronounced peaks of copper. This result suggests that the biosorbed copper was retained at the surface of the microbial cell.

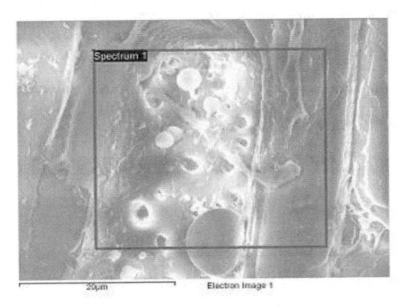

Figure 2.7. Attachment of bacteria onto the wood husk (magnification 2500 x).

Table 2.2. EDAX analysis

Element	App	Intensity	Weight%	Weight%	Atomic%
C K	70.47	1.4577	54.00	1.29	61.89
O K	35.67	0.9109	43.73	1.29	37.62
Cu L	0.97	0.4771	2.27	0.63	0.49
Total			100.00		

CONCLUSION

The ability of a bacterial consortium consisting of *A. haemolyticus* and *E.coli* to remove Cr(VI), Cu(II) and Ni(II) ions from aqueous solution has been demonstrated. The ability of *A. haemolyticus* to utilize LPW as a nutrient is an excellent example of the substitution of a cheap and readily available industrial waste in place of expensive growth medium and could be a significant factor for use in a commercial process. The following conditions are useful for the metal removal process: Cr(VI) - pH 2, 10 h contact time, Cr(VI) ≥ 400 mg L^{-1}, HCl-treated cells, Cu(II) − pH 5, 10 h contact time, useful for both the simulated and industrial effluents and for Ni(II) − 10 h contact time, Ni(II) < 400 mg L^{-1}, cell concentration of 0.2 g L^{-1}, pH 6 and NaOH-treated cells.

ACKNOWLEDGMENTS

The authors acknowledge the contributions by the Ministry of Science, Technology and Innovation, Malaysia, for funding the project via the TechnoFund grant (TF0106B001). A special note of thanks to Lee Pineapple, Tampoi, for providing the liquid pineapple waste. Also to Mr. Jefri Samin (Department of Material Science, Faculty of Mechanical Engineering) for his expertise in the electron microscopy works.

REFERENCES

Anjana, K., Kaushik, A., Kiran, B. and Nisha, R.(2007). "Biosorption of Cr(VI) by immobilized biomass of two indigenous strains of cyanobacteria isolated from contaminated soil." *Journal of Hazardous Materials.* 148. 383-386.

Bueno, B.Y.M, Torem, M.L, Molina, F. and de Mesquita, L.M.S. (2008). "Biosorption of lead(II), chromium(III) and copper(II) by *R. Opacus*: Equilibrium and kinetic studies." *Minerals Engineering.* 21: 65-75.

Daulton, T.L., Little, B.J., Jones-Meehan, J., Blom, D.A and Allard, L.F. (2007). "Microbial reduction of chromium from the hexavalent to divalent state." *Geochimica.* 71. 556–565.

Go´mez, V. and Callao, M.P. (2006). "Chromium determination and speciation since 2000." *Trends in Analytical Chemistry.* 25: 1006-1015.

Greenberg, A.E., Trussell, R.R. and Clesceri, L.S. "Standards methods for the examination of water and wastewater." 16th Ed. New York. American Public Health Association. 1998.

Han, X., Wong, Y.K., Wong, M.H. and Tam, N.F.Y.(2007). "Biosorption and bioreduction of Cr(VI) by a microalgal isolate, *Chlorella miniata.*" *Journal of Hazardous Materials.* 146. 65-72.

Kotas, J. and Stasicka, Z. (2000). "Chromium occurrence in the environment and methods of its speciation." *Environmental Pollution.* 107. 263-283.

Li, H., Liu, T., Li, Z. and Deng, L. (2007). "Low-cost supports used to immobilize fungi and reliable technique for removal hexavalent chromium in wastewater." *Bioresource Technology.* 99: 2234-2241.

Madigan, M.T., Martinko, J.M. and Parker, J. "Brock Biology of Microrganisms." 8th Ed 1997. Prentice-Hall.

Mashitah, M.D., Yus Azila, Y. and Bhatia, S. (2008). "Biosorption of cadmium (II) ions by immobilized cells of *Pycnoporus sanguineus* from aqueous solution." *Bioresource Technology.* 99: 4742-4748.

Mecozzi, M. (2005). "Estimation of total carbohydrate amount in environmental samples by the phenol–sulphuric acid method assisted by multivariate calibration." *Chemometrics and Intelligent Laboratory Systems.* 79. 84 – 90.

Mungasavalli, D.P., Viraraghavan, T. and Jin Y.C. (2007). "Biosorption of chromium from aqueous solutions by pretreated *Aspergillus niger*: Batch and column studies." *Colloids and Surfaces A: Physicochem. Eng. Aspects.* 301. 214–223.

Thacker, U., Parikh, R., Shouche, Y. and Madamwar, D.(2007). "Reduction of chromate by cell-free extract of *Brucella* sp. Isolated from Cr(VI) contaminated sites." *Bioresource Technology.* 98. 1541-1547.

Tunali, S., Kiran, I. and Akar, T. (2005). "Chromium (VI) biosorption Characteristics of *Neurospora crassa* Fungal Biomass." *Minerals Engineering.* 18. 681-689.

Zakaria, Z.A. "Development of bacterial-based remediation system for the removal of chromium (VI) from electroplating industrial effluent." PhD Thesis. Universiti Teknologi Malaysia, 2006.

In: Bacteria in Environmental Biotechnology   ISBN 978-1-61728-350-5
Editor: W. A. Ahmad et al.   © 2011 Nova Science Publishers, Inc.

Chapter 3

REMOVAL OF TOXIC AND PRECIOUS METALS FROM MINING AND PHOTOGRAPHIC EFFLUENTS USING MINES-TAILINGS ISOLATED BACTERIA

Saffiah Abdullah Khir, Hanisom Abdullah
and Roslindawati Haron

ABSTRACT

Eighteen Gram negative bacteria and five Gram positive bacteria has been successfully isolated from the mines tailings. *Thiobacillus ferrooxidans* (*T. ferrooxidans*) was isolated from the acidic mine water and characterized using the 16S rRNA method. Isolate A and P were used during the removal of Zn(II) and Cu(II), *T. ferrooxidans* for Au while *P. diminuta* for Ag. The ability of the bacterial isolates to tolerate the toxicity of the mines tailings promises its suitability in the metal removal process. High Au, Ag, Zn and Cu uptake capacity in both the batch and flow-through column system indicate the potential application of the bacterial process as an alternative to the currently practiced methods. The ability to recover the adsorbed metals using different kinds of available eluting agents enhanced the ability of processes such as this.

INTRODUCTION

The urgency to recover heavy metals can be based on its environmental risk and its diminishing commercial value due to depletion of reserves at a high rate (Volesky, 1987, 1999). These factors can be an indication of the future demand of metals, for example, Cd, Hg and Pb. If based on environmental risk alone, all three would be considered as high priority to be recovered. However, in terms of technological use, Hg and Pb are increasingly being overlooked while more attention is focused on Cd. Eccles (1999) has stated that liquid-effluent treatment processes have to be more robust than the manufacturing process itself. In an ideal condition, the effluent treatment process should be compatible with existing technique, cost effective, robust, reliable, simple and highly selective. This is because, normally, real effluent varies in terms of quantity and quality, even if it originates from the same source of discharge. Variations encountered can be of the chemical and physical characteristics, pH, and presence of inorganic and organic compounds, dissolved and volatile species, colloids, emulsion and particles. The use of existing technologies such as activated carbon and ion-exchanger are expensive and normally not selective. Lime precipitation would create a secondary waste disposal problem in terms of amounts of sludge generated. In view of this complication, it can be predicted that the amounts of money involved in dealing with waste disposal and recovery would increase in the future.

This justifies the need for an alternative treatment technology. Generally, this "new" technology should have the same basic design, operation mode, similar if not better performance, and be cheaper than the available conventional methods. For this purpose, microorganisms do offer great potential in becoming a potent yet effective metal-adsorbing material. Microorganisms are known to have a natural metal-sequestering ability whether through surface adsorption or intracellular accumulation. However, the nature of metal uptake is usually dependent on the species and metals to be recovered. A continuous, thorough, serious and detailed study is required to obtain the optimum species that should be highly selective and robust enough to fit any possible waste types. For example, the species should be useful to selectively recover any metallic species intended from a multi-metallic solution in one situation while at the same time should also be compatible when required to remove more than one metallic species from solution or effluent.

ISOLATION OF BACTERIA FROM MINES TAILINGS AND ACIDIC MINE WATER

Effluent samples were collected from five different sites in the tailings dam (Figure 3.1). Sterilized universal bottles containing NB, NB (8 g L^{-1}) were used to transfer the bacteria. Parameters such as pH, dissolved oxygen and temperature were monitored. All samples were aerated, and bacterial growth was monitored daily. The bacteria were isolated using Nutrient Agar (NA). Mixed colonies that grew on the NA plates were serially subcultured until a single pure colony of bacterium was obtained. Pure bacterial isolate was then determined for its motility, Gram feature and growth profile. These pure bacterial colonies obtained were then subcultured in Glycerol-Glycerophosphate Medium (GGM) and Chloride-Free Medium (CFM). Growth profiles for isolates that could grow in both GGM and CFM were recorded.

Acid mine water samples were collected from different sites of the Au mine. The pH and temperature values were recorded. The mine water samples were aseptically inoculated into sterile universal bottles containing various concentrations of Fe (II) ion in sulphate form / basal salts medium as described in Table 3.1.

Following this, the isolation of pure colonies of iron-oxidizing bacteria was made on various solid media as described in Table 3.2. Growth and morphology of the colonies that grew on the solid media were compared to that of control culture 7'. *T.ferrooxidans* DSM 583 obtained from Deutsche Sammlung von. Mikroorganismen und Zellkulturen (DSMZ), Germany.

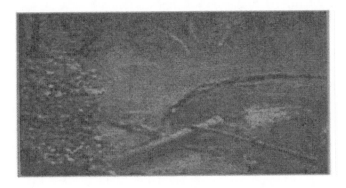

Figure 3.1. One of the sites for effluent sampling located at the tailings dam.

Table 3.1. Concentration of Fe (II) ion and pH in each Fe (II) sulphate / basal salts liquid media

	$[Fe^{2+}]$, g L^{-1}	pH
Fe (II) sulphate/ basal salts	3.0 - 14.0	2.0
Supplemented with yeast extract	3.0	2.0
9K medium	44.22	1.8 - 2.0

Table 3.2. Properties of solid media used in the isolation of pure cultures

Media	Content	Final pH	°C
FeTSB	Basal salts, $FeSO_4$, gelling solution	2.2 - 2.3	30
FePo	FeTSB, K_2HPO_4, basal salts	2.2 - 2.3	30
FeTSBo	Basal salts, gelling solution, $FeSO_4$	2.5	30

The identification of the isolate PMINT 1 by the 16S rRNA analysis was performed by DSMZ of Germany. The bacteria was then characterized using two different methods: growth in Fe (II) ions and determination of cell protein by the Folin-Ciocalteau (Lowry) assay. Growth of the bacterial cultures was measured indirectly by their ability to oxidize Fe (II) ions using the $KMnO_4$ titration method. Cell protein determination was carried out using a modified Folin-Ciocalteu (Lowry) assay method. The method was based on colour formation due to reactions between protein-Folin-Ciocalteu reagent used and protein-alkaline copper used.

Selected bacterial isolates from the mines tailings were grown in GGM containing increasing concentrations of Au and Ag using the repli-plate technique (Sterilin, USA). Each culture was measured at OD_{600} using a spectrophotometer. Turbidity obtained was expressed as relative to turbidity in the control wells. The above procedure was also carried out for bacteria isolated from the acidic mine water area. The only difference being the Fe (II) sulphate/ basal salts medium used, addition of more metal ions to be examined, namely, As, Fe, Cu and Zn and determination of residual Fe (II) ions using the $KMnO_4$ titration method at the end of the incubation period.

Twenty-three morphologically distinct colony types have been isolated from effluent samples of the tailings dam. The conditions of pH and dissolved oxygen were permissible for bacterial growth. The bacteria were characterized based on its growth curve, motility and Gram stain profiles. Results from the Gram staining and motility test show that eighteen strains were found to be Gram negative while five were Gram positive. Most of the Gram negative isolates were cocci in shape and four of the isolated Gram positive bacteria were rod shaped. All isolates were motile based on observations from the hanging-drop technique. Further examination on the motility of bacteria was not carried out. Based on turbidity value obtained, Isolates F and N showed a better growth profile in CFM while isolates A and P grew better in GGM.

Results from the 16S rRNA analysis revealed that isolate PMINT 1 shows high sequence similarity of 99.6% to *T. ferrooxidans* N-Fe2 and of 99.0% to *T. ferrooxidans* Lp. These results and the phylogenetic tree indicate that the strain belongs to the *T. ferrooxidans* 16S rRNA cluster formed by strain N-Fe2 and Lp (Figure 3.2).

From the experiment, it was noted that with time, *T. ferrooxidans* and *T. ferrooxidans* DSM 583 showed an increasing trend of iron oxidation. In contrast, control containing sterile Fe (II) sulphate (14 g L^{-1})/ basal salts solution showed negligible oxidation.

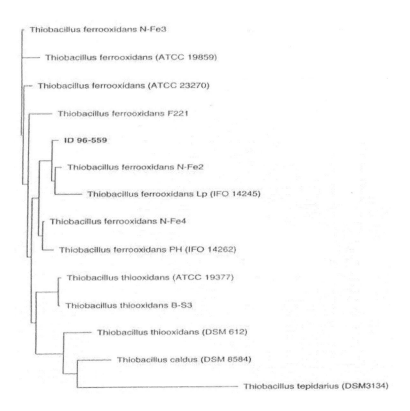

Figure 3.2. Phylogenetic tree of isolate PMINT 1 isolated from the acidic mine water.

The Fe (II) oxidation of the iron-oxidizers had lag phases ranging from approximately 6 to 12 h, with *T. ferrooxidans* being the slowest of the two, i.e., 12 h of lag phase. It was also noted that after 27 h, *T. ferrooxidans* DSM 583 reached to only 50% of Fe (II) oxidized by *T. ferrooxidans*. Furthermore, *T. ferrooxidans* DSM 583 completed Fe (II) oxidation within approximately 30 h, whilst T ferrooxidans required a further 10 h. Doubling times for *T. ferrooxidans* and *T ferrooxidans* DSM 583 were also determined to be 9.2 and 7.5 h, respectively.

Cell protein determination was carried out to further verify the use of Fe (II) oxidation as indicator for bacterial growth. The results showed that the cell protein concentration increased with increasing amount of Fe (II) oxidized. It was observed that both cells grew better in the 9K medium, which contained 44.2 g L^{-1} of Fe (II) sulphate in basal salts compared to 3.0 - 14.0 g L^{-1} of Fe (II) sulphate in basal salts. The ability of the isolates to tolerate high concentrations of heavy metals is essential for their exploitation for metal accumulation properties. Au and Ag were chosen because they were found to be naturally present in the tailings dam where the isolates were originally isolated. The tolerance level of these isolates is summarized in Table 3.3.

Overall, all isolates have relatively low tolerance level towards Au (III). Of the four isolates, isolate N appeared to be the most tolerant. On the other hand, almost all isolates were sensitive to Ag (I). It was reported that Ag is probably the most toxic metal to microorganisms. Some toxic effects of Ag to microorganisms are as follows: by displacing native metals from their normal binding sites or by binding to proteins and nucleic acids and altering their conformation. Ag also affects oxidative phosphorylation and membrane permeability of the microbes (Hughes and Poole, 1989). Ag salts, especially Ag nitrate, were once used as an antibacterial agent against gonococcal ophthalmological infections in newborn, topical prophylaxis against Pseudomonas infections and burns (Hughes and Poole, 1989).

Table 3.3. The tolerance level of isolate P, F, A and N towards Au and Ag ions

Isolate	Tolerance levels (mM)	
	Au (III)	Ag (I)
P	5.0	-
F	5.0	50.0
A	5.0	-
N	50.0	-

Ag Uptake Study

P. diminuta, a gram negative, short, rod-shaped bacteria, isolated from a copper mine in Sabah, was used throughout this study. Three types of cells were used, namely, treated, untreated and immobilized cells. NaOH was used to prepare the treated cell, while the untreated cell was left suspended in deionized water. Strontium alginate was used to immobilized cells of *P. diminuta*. The particle size of both the treated and untreated cell was then determined using a series of sieves with mesh sizes ranging from 75 to 300 pm. For the treated and untreated cells, $AgNO_3$ solution was used as simulated effluent for Ag^+ ions. Different experimental fractions obtained, i.e., supernatant, deionized water washed, acid washed and pellet digest were analyzed for Ag using Atomic Absorption Spectroscopy (AAS). For the immobilized cell, Ag^+ ions were used between 10 to 1000 mg L^{-1}. The presence of residual Ag ions was analyzed using AAS. Kinetic study was also carried out by varying the reaction time. Desorption of Ag was carried out using various eluting solutions, namely, HNO_3, NH_4NO_3 - NH_3, KI and $Na_2S_2O_3.5H_2O$.

Different fractions of the effluents were collected from a photo-processing studio in Kulai, Johor. The fractions are paper developer, paper bleach, film bleach, film developer, film stabilizer and film fixer. These fractions differed in colour, pH and Ag content. For practical reasons, only the film fixer was used in the Ag uptake experiment. The effect of varying cell particle size and initial Ag concentrations on the overall uptake of Ag was also considered. Both the alginate and biobeads were mixed with 500 mg L^{-1} of $AgNO_3$ solution for 1 h at 30 °C. Then, the mixture was filtered using Whatman filter paper to remove residual Ag^+. Bound Ag on the biobeads was desorped using 10 mL of 0.1 M HNO_3 for 1 h at 30 °C. Biobeads with Ag^+, biobeads with Ag^+ and desorped with 0.1 M HNO_3, and biobeads not exposed to Ag^+ (acted as control) were then prepared for TEM analysis. Prior to sectioning, samples were prefixed in 2.5% (v/v) glutaraldehyde for 4 h. After thorough rinsings, samples were then post-fixed in 2% (w/w) osmium tetroxide for 1 h. Dehydration of the samples was carried out using increasing concentrations of alcohol (40 to 100%). Further dehydration was achieved by infiltration in propylene oxide followed by embedment in Epoxy resin. The resultant blocks after polymerization were trimmed accordingly prior to ultra-thin sectioning (90 to 100 mm thick) using a Sorvall MT-2B ultramicrotome.

Table 3.4. Ag uptake by free, treated and untreated cells of P

Type of cell	Uptake, μmol Ag$^+$ g^{-1} dry wt.
Free	216
Treated	101
Untreated	35

Sections were stained with 3 % (v/v) uranyl acetate for 7 mins and counter-stained with 2 to 3% (w/v) lead nitrate for another 5 mins. The stained sections were then mounted onto copper grids and viewed using the Hitachi H-300 transmission electron microscope.

Ag content determined from the supernatant, water wash, acid wash and pellet digest fractions is representative of free metal, loosely bound metal, tightly bound and intracellular accumulation, respectively (Table 3.4).

From Table 3.5, it was clear that free cells exhibited the highest Ag uptake capacity compared with the treated and untreated cells. However, the result seems to disagree with the findings of Brierley (1990), where treated *Bacillus subtilis* cell showed a higher Ag loading than the untreated cell. A possible explanation for this discrepency is the type of cells used; *B. subtilis* is a Gram positive bacteria while *P. diminuta* is a Gram negative strain. Immobilized cells showed a high capacity of Ag removal with a value of more than 800 μmol g^{-1} dry wt. compared with around 50 μmol g^{-1} dry wt for free cell (in the same experiment) at an initial concentration of Ag at 1000 mg L^{-1}. However, free cell showed a better uptake capacity at lower concentrations (10 to 200 mg L^{-1}) compared to immobilized cell, which was more prominent in the higher concentration region. For immobilized cell, no distinct saturation condition was observed, which would suggest the possibility of tolerating a higher concentration of Ag in solution. The kinetic study revealed that within the incubation period of 1 h, higher amounts of Ag were accumulated by free cells compared to the immobilized cell. It was also observed that prolonged incubation decreases the Ag uptake value. Table 3.5 shows the Ag uptake profile by treated and untreated cells of *P. diminuta* at different particle size.

From Table 3.5, it was clearly observed that the Ag removal capacity for untreated cell is higher than the treated cell. Maximum uptake for the untreated cell was around 22 μmol Ag g^{-1} dry wt. at cell particle size of 150 to 212 μm, compared to around 11 μmol Ag g^{-1} dry wt. for the treated cell. It is also worthy to note that the amounts of Ag removed from the simulated effluent were higher than that of the photographic effluent.

Table 3.5. Ag uptake profile by treated and untreated cells of *P. diminuta* at different particle size

Cell size (µm)	Uptake, µmol Ag^+ g^{-1} dry wt.	
	Treated cell	Untreated cell
< 75	4	18
75 - 150	8	19
150 - 212	11	22
212 - 300	14	20
> 300	13	18

This could be due to the variation in the speciation of Ag present in the photographic effluent. Ag may exist in its cationic form or complexes with thiosulphate. Besides that, other components present, such as sodium sulphite, acetic acid and potassium alum, can also interfere in maximum removal of Ag ions. Both cell exhibits an increasing Ag uptake profile with an increase in the initial Ag concentrations prepared in solution. Figure 3.3 shows the TEM micrographs obtained from the alginate beads study. It was noted that the alginate beads exposed to 500 mg L^{-1} Ag^+ (Figure 3.3a) appeared darker and more elongated than the control, i.e., without Ag^+ (Figure 3.3b). There was a reduction in the amounts of Ag (seen as electron dense structures) when treated with 0.1 M HNO_3 (Figure 3.3c).

Another interesting feature to be noted is the shrinkage of alginate structures, which could be due to acid. In this work, immobilization technique chosen was entrapment of cells in alginate. The TEM micrographs showed clearly the presence of cells within the alginate matrix (Figure 3.4a). The distribution of the cells was, however, uneven. While most of the Ag was bound on the cell surface, the micrograph also seemed to suggest some deposition of Ag inside the cells. This could be due to the intrusion of cell into the biobeads resulting from a longer contact time. An uneven distribution of Ag inside the cell was also observed where some cells showed a solid electron-dense structure indicating Ag-laden condition (Figure 3.4b). The TEM study also revealed that cell maintained its rod-shaped like structure when entrapped with the alginate matrix. Upon desorption of the biobeads with 0.1 M HNO_3 (Figure 3.4c), the alginate seemed to shrink in size while the cell size was unaffected. A reduced intensity in the amount of electron dense particle could be indicative of removal of bound Ag by acid. The presence of Ag^+ traces on the biobeads may suggest the unsuitability of 0.1 M HNO_3 as an eluting agent for Ag.

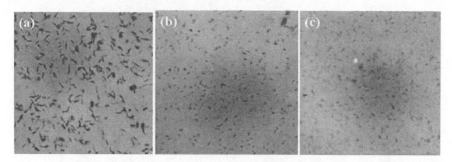

Figure 3.3. Electron micrographs of the alginate beads (a) exposed to 500 mg L^{-1} Ag$^+$ (b) control (without Ag$^+$) (c) after desorption using 0.1 M HNO$_3$.

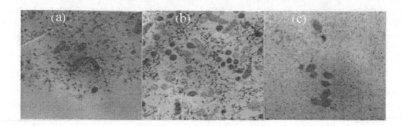

Figure 3.4. Electron micrographs of the *P. diminuta* cells entrapped in the alginate beads (a) control (without Ag$^+$) (b) exposed to 500 mg L^{-1} Ag$^+$ (c) after desorption using 0.1 M HNO$_3$.

AU UPTAKE STUDY (U FOR AU SHOULD BE IN LOWER CASE AND NOT CAPITAL U)

In this study, *T. ferrooxidans*, which was isolated from a local gold mine in Terengganu, was used as the biosorbent. It was sent to DSMZ, Germany for identification. Growth medium used for the cultivation of *T. ferrooxidans* was the 9K medium. The 9K medium is a mixture between the $FeSO_4$ and basal salts solution. $FeSO_4$ solution was prepared by dissolving $FeSO4.7H_2O$ (147.33 g L^{-1}) in deionized water to give a final concentration of Fe^{2+} ion at 0.106 M. The pH was adjusted to 1.90 (Horiba, F-12) using concentrated H_2SO_4. It was then filter sterilized using a 0.45 μm Whatman filter paper. Basal salts used contained the following components, (per liter deionized water); $(NH_4)_2SO_4$, 4.29 g, KCl, 0.14 g, K_2HPO_4, 0.14 g and $MgSO_4.7H_2O$, 0.71 g. It was then acidified to a pH of 2.0 using concentrated H_2SO_4. Following this, the mixture was sterilized by autoclaving (Fedegari, Italy) at

121 °C, 126 kPa for 15 mins. Mines tailings used in this study were obtained from the Lubuk Mandi gold Mine tailings dam. The tailing consists of 58% liquid and 42% solids. Due to the deleterious effect of CN, the determination of CN content in the tailings was performed. The mines tailings were also analyzed for its metal composition where the aqueous portion was analyzed for Ag, Au, Cd, Cu, Fe, Pb and Zn using AAS.

A modified procedure from Wakao et al. (1994) was used in the treatment of *T. ferrooxidans* with acid and heat, hence termed as SP and SPHT cells, respectively. Stationary phase cells were first harvested by centrifugation (SIGMA 4K15, B.Braun) at 1028 rpm, 10 mins and 0 °C to remove any possible iron precipitates from the solution. The pellet was discarded while the supernatant centrifuged at 8225 rpm, 10 mins and 0 °C. The pellet was then washed three times with H_2SO_4 (pH 1.5) and rinsed two times with deionized water at 8225 rpm, 3 mins and 0 °C. Finally, it was resuspended in a small volume of deionized water. For the preparation of SPHT cells, the cell suspension was autoclaved (Fedegari, Italy) at 121 °C, 126 kPa for 15 mins. The dry weight of cells was determined by filtering 5 mL of culture through pre-weighed cellulose filters (pore size 0.45 μm), which had been dried at 105 °C for 18 h to constant weight.

For the kinetic study, cells of *T. ferrooxidans* (1.0 mg) were mixed with Au solution (100 mg L^{-1}) at pH 2.0 and were equilibrated for 1 h. The mixture was pelleted by centrifugation where the filtrate was analyzed for Au using AAS. The rate of Au uptake was determined by the ratio between the initial and residual Au concentrations. In the uptake study, 1.0 mg cell of *T. ferrooxidans* was mixed with various initial concentrations of Au (5 to 100 mg L^{-1}) at pH 2.0. A control experiment was prepared, comprising all of the above, minus the cells. All results obtained were evaluated using simple adsorption isotherms, namely, Langmuir, Freundlich and BET. The experiment was conducted to assess the performance of both the SP and SPHT cells in the uptake of Au from mines tailings used. In this experiment, the kinetic and uptake profiles of Au by *T. ferrooxidans* were derived from a single set of experiments and not through a series of experiments. Cell suspension of *T. ferrooxidans* (1.0 mg) was mixed with tailings and left to equilibrate. The filtrate was analyzed for Au using AAS. The amount of Au adsorped was determined by the difference between the initial and residual concentrations. Mines tailings was determined for its cyanide content and metallic species present in the solid and liquid fractions. NaOH treatment would remove certain protein components from the bacterial cell wall, which could possibly act as metal-binding sites, hence reducing the overall capacity of the metal uptake. The cyanide content of the mines tailings was treated using the UV-irradiation, as shown in Figure 3.5.

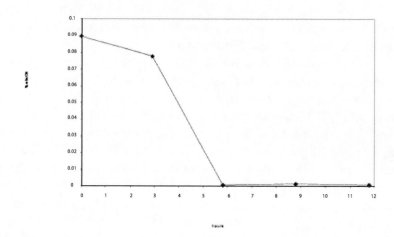

Figure 3.5. Cyanide degradation in mines tailings by UV-irradiation.

Upon 29 h of UV-irradiation, a near complete cyanide degradation was achieved. Concentration of cyanide has decreased by a factor of 12 fold, that is from 0.0897% (w/w) to 0.007% (w/w). The degradation of cyanide can be assessed by the formation of CO_2 and NH_3 as the breakdown product. This can be explained according to Equation 3.1. The absence of cyanide was further supported by the presence of $BaCO_3$, as white precipitates upon addition of $Ba(OH)_2$, which confirmed the presence of CO_2, i.e., the breakdown product of cyanide. Results from the analysis conducted for the solid and liquid portions of the mines tailings are shown in Table 3.6 and 3.7, respectively.

$$2CN^- + O_2 + 4H_2O \; \rightarrow 2CO_3^{2-} + 2NH_4^+ \qquad\qquad \text{(Equation 3.1)}$$

Table 3.6. Elemental analysis for solid portions of Lubuk Mandi Gold Mine tailings

Elements	mg kg^{-1} solid
Au	2.06
Cd	0.68
Cu	7.68
Fe	>90%
Zn	34.50

Table 3.7. Elemental analysis for liquid portions of Lubuk Mandi Gold Mine tailings

Elements	mg L^{-1} liquid		
	Point 1	Point 2	Point 3
Au	0.08	0.06	0.06
Cd	ND	ND	ND
Cu	0.14	0.04	0.22
Fe	0.12	0.33	5.50
Zn	0.46	0.43	1.52
*pH	5.29	5.46	3.97

From Tables 3.6 and 3.7, it was observed that the concentrations of Fe and Zn were notably higher than other elements. The concentrations of metals were also higher in the solid portions compared with the liquid portions. A plausible explanation is the neutral pH of the tailings (around 7 to 8), which hindered the dissolution of metals present in the solid fraction. Point 1 refers to the main tailings site containing fresh and stacked processed gold ore. Point 2 is the intermediate area or as containment pond for overflow from point 1, while point 3 is the last point before the run-off water from the tailings sites enters the nearby river for disposal. Here, KOH was added to maintain the pH at near neutral level. It is worth noting that the concentration of metals seems to increase upon reaching point 3 of sampling. This could be due to, firstly, the dispersion or sedimentation of metals from adsorption by natural organic and inorganic material or, secondly, the seepage of metals to the underground water system, which results in the decrease of metals (point 1 to 2). However, upon reaching point 3, flocculation and precipitation of metals by KOH added brings the adsorped metallic species back into the water system (point 3). This was not the case for gold, where a constant concentration has been observed. This would support the fewer occurrences of gold species in liquid forms compared to its solid form.

In this chapter, two support materials were used, namely, polyurethane foam and loofa sponge. The degree of bacterial immobilization on the support was derived from the Au biosorption experiment. Results obtained showed that polyurethane foam was not suitable for immobilization of isolate F. Less amount of bacteria was bound as a result of cell leakage into the residual solution. Leakage of metal-loaded cells in the residual solution also led to misinterpretation of the results. Au uptake for the immobilized bacteria was not possibly calculated.

Table 3.8. Profiles of parameters involved in Au uptake by isolate F

Set	Eluant	Uptake (mg g^{-1} dry wt.)		% Elution	
		Control	Test	Control	Test
1	Thiourea (0.5 M, pH 1.9)	0.0137	0.0220	53.33	42.29
2	Thiourea (0.5 M, pH 5.24)	0.0158	0.0205	32.28	57.77
3	Thiourea (0.5 M) + FeCl$_3$ (0.02 M)	0.0168	0.0212	44.69	50.00
4	Thiourea (0.5 M) + FeCl$_3$ (0.2 M)	0.0146	0.0196	51.56	73.78

On this basis, the possibility of using polyurethane foam as support was rejected. Results from Au biosorption using loofa sponge are shown in Table 3.8.

In conclusion, loofa sponge provides a better support material to immobilize bacteria than polyurethane foam. From the AAS analysis, a total amount of 37.83% Au (control) and 25.24% Au (test) was successfully recovered from the elution fraction after 30 mins of electrolysis. The difference in weight of the cathode before and after electrolysis was 2.5 mg (test) and 8.3 mg (control).

RECOVERY OF Zn AND Cu FROM MINES TAILINGS

Two locally isolated Gram negative bacteria, namely, isolates A and P, were used. It was grown in GGM. Sand was chosen as the supporting material for immobilization of isolate A and P. The sand was treated using a procedure modified from Heiskanen and Yao (1992). Sand was first mixed with 2M HCl for 6 h and rinsed with deionized water until a pH of around 2 was achieved. The treated sand was then left to dry overnight at 60 °C. Particle size determination was carried out using test-sieve shaker (ETL – 2 - mk 3).

The sand-packed column was first rinsed with deionized water until a clear effluent was obtained. Cell suspension containing 1.0 mg of cells was introduced into the column using peristaltic pump. Deionized water rinsing was carried out to remove loosely bound cells. Both mines tailings and simulated effluent were passed through the column in a downward flow using peristaltic pump.

Table 3.9. Profiles for maximum Cu uptake from simulated and mines tailings by isolates A and P

pH	Isolate A		Isolate P	
	Simulated	Tailings	Simulated	Tailings
1.5	-	14.40	-	10.66
4.5	5745.60	23.24	4796.20	13.28

*Values in mg g^{-1} cell dry wt.

Effluent collected was measured for Zn and Cu content using AAS. The amount of Zn and Cu adsorped was determined by the difference between the initial and residual concentrations of each metal in the mines tailings. Desorption of the metals was attempted using HNO_3. Based on the analysis conducted, an amount of 0.998 mg cell dry wt. (99.8%) of bacteria A and 1.0 mg cell dry wt. (100%) of bacteria P was successfully immobilized on the sand. This strengthens the suitability of sand as supporting matrix for bacteria (Heiskanen and Yao, 1992). An increase of around 200-fold in Cu uptake was observed when simulated Cu effluent was used instead of mines tailings (Table 3.9).

In this study, the Cu uptake study using mines tailings was carried out first before proceeding with simulated effluent. From Table 3.10, it was also shown that the amounts of Cu removed from solution were greater at pH 4.5 compared to pH 1.5 for both isolates A and P; hence, pH 4.5 was used in the mines tailings study. This situation could be due to the effect of pH on the stability of ionic metallic species in solution, the concentration of hydrogen ions and the chemical structure of binding sites on the bacteria. For example, at an acidic pH, the high concentration of H^+ ions in solution would compete with any metallic species for binding sites on the bacterial surface. The presence of other metallic species in the mines tailings also undermine the role of these ions in competing with Cu for binding sites. This statement is supported from result shown from the simulated effluent experiment where, in the absence of other competing metallic ions, the amount of Cu removed increased significantly. Table 3.10 shows the Cu breakthrough profiles for both isolates A and P at pH 1.5 and 4.5, respectively.

From Table 3.10, it was observed that at pH 1.5, the column was fully saturated with Cu (Ceq / Ci = 1.0) but not at pH 4.5, where the Ceq/ Ci value obtained was around 0.6 only. This indicated the higher affinity of isolate A towards Cu at pH 4.5 than at pH 1.5 compared to isolate P.

Table 3.10. Profiles for Cu breakthrough for simulated and mines tailings by isolates A and P

pH	Isolate A		Isolate P	
	Simulated	Tailings	Simulated	Tailings
1.5	-	1.00	-	1.00
4.5	0.51	0.60	0.44	0.60

*Values shown as ratio between C_{eq} (mg L^{-1}) over C_i (mg L^{-1}).

Table 3.11. Profiles for Zn uptake study from mines tailings and simulated effluent using isolates A and P

pH	Isolate A		Isolate P	
	Simulated	Tailings	Simulated	Tailings
1.5	-	14.81	-	14.81
4.5	1461.60	205.30	1103.60	58.20

*Values in ng g^{-1} cell dry wt.

It was also noticed that at pH 4.5, the rate of Cu uptake by isolate A was higher than isolate P. Table 3.11 shows the profile obtained for Zn uptake study from mines tailings and simulated effluent using isolate A and P.

From Table 3.11, it was noted that the amounts of Zn removed from solution was higher for the simulated effluent compared with the mines tailings, comparable with results obtained from the Cu uptake experiment. From the Zn uptake profiles (data not shown), it was observed that at pH 4.5, the amounts of Zn removed increased with increasing tailings volume. For pH 1.5, the same trend was also observed but only at low tailings volume, where no further Zn removal was recorded when the tailings volume was increased. This shows an effective Zn removal at pH 4.5, which correlated well with results reported by other researchers (Dursun et al., 2000; Kutsal et al., 2000). At this pH, Zn (II) ions bind electrostatically with the negatively charged binding sites on the bacterial surface. However, at a higher pH, Zn (II) ions will be precipitated as its hydroxide ions (Equation 3.2).

$$Zn^{2+} + 4OH^- \leftrightarrow Zn(OH)_4^{2-}$$ (Equation 3.2)

CONCLUSION

Eighteen Gram negative bacteria and five Gram positive bacteria have been successfully isolated from the mines tailings with four species; A, P, F and N showed better growth profile in CFM and GGM medium used. From the acid mine water, the species *T. ferrooxidans* was isolated and characterized using the 16S rRNA method. *T. ferrooxidans* showed the tendency to grow better in 9K medium than other $FeSO_4$-basal salts mixture. The ability of the bacterial isolates to tolerate the toxicity of the mines tailings promises its suitability in the metal removal process. High Au, Ag, Zn and Cu uptake capacity of the isolates indicate the potential application of the bacterial process as an alternative to the currently practiced methods.

ACKNOWLEDGMENTS

The authors acknowledge the financial contributions from the Ministry of Science and Technology (MOSTE), Malaysia. Also to Sumber Lubuk Minerals (PERMINT), Terengganu. Our sincere gratitude is also extended to the Pejabat Harta Bina and the Faculty of Science, UTM for logistical assistance.

REFERENCES

Brierley, C.L. (1990) "Metal Immobilization Using Bacteria" in Ehrlich, H.E. and Brierley, C.L. (eds.). Microbial Mineral Recovery. McGraw-Hill Publishing Company. USA.

Eccles, H. (1999) "Treatment of metal-contaminated wastes: why select a biological process" Trends in Biotechnology. Elsevier Science Ltd.. 17:12. Dec 99. London. UK.

Heiskanen, K. and Yao, L. (1992) "Finely ground waste rock as an adsorption material for anionic collectors" in Anthony, M. (ed.). Minerals, Metals and the Environment. Elsevier, London. 407-419.

Hughes, M.N. and Poole, R.K. (1989) "Metals and Microorganisms" Chapman and Hall. UK.

Volesky, B. (1987) "Biosorbents for Metal Recovery" Trends in Biotechnology. Elsevier Publications. *Cambridge. Apr.* 5: 96-101.

Volesky, B. (1999b) "Biosorption for the Next Century" in Proceedings of International Biohydrometallurgy Symposium IBS'99; Part B: Molecular Biology. Biosorption and Bioremediation. in Amils, R. and Ballester, A. (eds.). Elsevier Science.

Wakao, N., Endo, K., Mino, K. and Sakurai, Y. (1994) "Immobilization of *Thiobacillus ferrooxidans* Using Various Polymers as Matrix" *J. Gen. Appl. Microbiology.* 40: 349- 358.

In: Bacteria in Environmental Biotechnology   ISBN 978-1-61728-350-5
Editor: W. A. Ahmad et al.   © 2011 Nova Science Publishers, Inc.

Chapter 4

REMOVAL OF CHROMIUM (VI) USING CHITOSAN-IMMOBILIZED *ACINETOBACTER HAEMOLYTICUS*

Rozidaini Mohd Ghazi and Zainoha Zakaria

ABSTRACT

In Malaysia, chitin can be found in abundance from the waste products of the seafood industry. It can be easily converted to chitosan (its derivative), which has high adsorption capacity for metal ions. One locally isolated bacterium, *Acinetobacter haemolyticus*, has been reported to be a potent chelator for the Cr(VI) ions. In this chapter, *A. haemolyticus* was immobilized into chitosan, and the newly formed bioparticle was assessed for its Cr(VI) removal capacity. Maximum Cr(VI) removal by the chitosan-immobilized *A. haemolyticus* was achieved at the following condition; (initial Cr(VI) of 300 mg L^{-1}), Qmax - 250 mg g^{-1}, pH 3, biosorbent dose of 5 mg, 6 hours of contact time. The biosorbent can be regenerated using 0.01 M H$_2$SO$_4$ after three biosorption-desorption cycles without any considerable loss in the biosorption capacity. The bioparticle (chitosan-immobilized *A. haemolyticus*) shows great potential to be applied for Cr(VI) removal from simulated effluent and electroplating wastewater.

INTRODUCTION

The presence of heavy metals in various water resources is of great concern since it is toxic to human beings, animals and plants. Heavy metals such as Pb, Cu, Cr, Zn, Ag, Hg and As must be removed from the wastewaters in order to meet the increasingly stringent environmental quality standards (Bailey et al., 1999. and Aziz et al., 2007). In the environment, chromium, a redox active metal element, usually exists as Cr(III) or Cr(VI) species. The Cr(VI) species may be in the form of dichromate ($Cr_2O_7^{2-}$), hydrochromate ($HCrO_4^-$), or chromate (CrO_4^{2-}), in a solution, depending on the pH (Namasivayam and Sureshkumar, 2008). Due to the repulsive electrostatic interactions, Cr(VI) anionic species are poorly adsorbed by the negatively charged soil particles in the environment, and hence, they can transfer freely in the aqueous environments. The Cr(III) species in aqueous solutions, however, may take the forms of Cr^{3+}, $Cr(OH)_2^+$, or $Cr(OH)_2^+$, depending on the solution pH. These positively charged species are relatively easy to be adsorbed on the negatively charged soil particles and thus are less mobile than Cr(VI) species in the environment (Namasivayam and Sureshkumar, 2008).

The conventional techniques most often used for the removal of toxic metals such as Cr from industrial effluents are reduction, precipitation, ion exchange osmosis and adsorption (Ahluwalia and Goyal, 2006). Except for adsorption, these conventional methods for wastewater treatment are not practical nowadays due to the production of toxic sludge and inability to remove trace levels of heavy metal ions from the wastewater. The production of low cost adsorbent is an alternative to remove the contamination of heavy metals in the wastewater. Babel and Kurniawan (2003) have reviewed the use of low-cost adsorbent such as chitosan derived from natural resources. In Malaysia, chitin can be found in abundance from the waste products of the seafood industry. Chitosan is a product of deacetylation of chitin using concentrated alkali at certain temperature (Cardenas et al., 2001). Chitosan adsorbs some metals quantitatively as oxyanions or anionic chloro complexes in sample solution by an ion exchange mechanism. The sorption of Cr(VI) does indeed occur on amine functional groups of the chitosan, as shown in Figure 4.1 (Boddu et al., 2003). This implies that the interaction occurs between NH_3^+ functional groups in chitosan and $Cr_2O_7^{2-}$ and that the interaction is chiefly electrostatic attraction in nature (Boddu et al., 2003).

Cross-linked chitosan gives rise to the phosphate groups that are negatively charged and can attract metal ions. The mechanism of the cross-linked chitosan is shown in Figure 4.2.

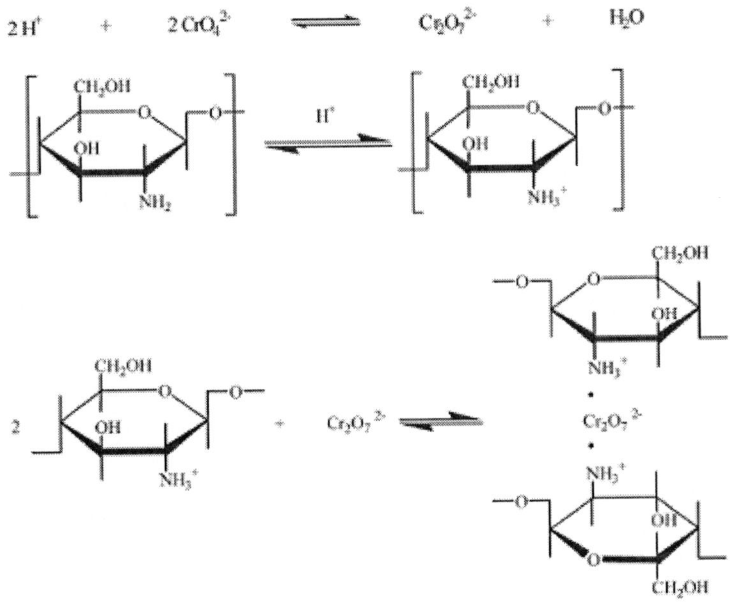

$$2H^+ \quad + \quad 2CrO_4^{2-} \quad \rightleftharpoons \quad Cr_2O_7^{2-} \quad + \quad H_2O$$

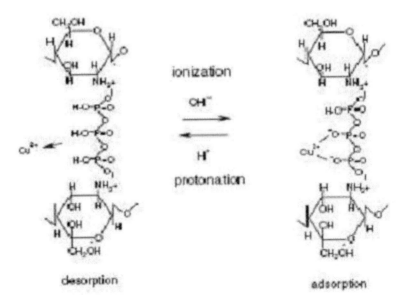

Figure 4.1. Sorption of Cr(VI) on amine functional group of the chitosan (Boddu et al., 2003).

Figure 4.2. Mechanism of metal ion uptake by cross-linked chitosan (Lee et al., 2001).

The use of biological materials, including living and non-living micro-organisms, in the removal and possibly recovery of toxic or precious metals from industrial wastes, has gained important credibility during recent years, because of the good performance and low cost of these materials (Sahin and Ozturk, 2005). However, the use of non-living microbial biomass in its native form for large-scale process is not practical because of its smaller particle size, low mechanical strength and difficulty of separation from the liquid stream. In view of this, it is of interest to use an immobilized form of these native biomasses to improve its mechanical strength and resistance to the various chemical constituents of aqueous waste (Bai and Abraham, 2003). The immobilization of bacteria, for example, could enhance the performance and adsorptive capacity of the biosorbent systems for heavy metal ions (Arica and Bayramoglu, 2005). Most studies regarding heavy metal uptake by immobilized bacteria reported on the use of sodium alginate (Anjana et al. 2007, Onal et al. 2007) or agarose (Bera et al. 2006) as immobilization matrix. The evaluation on other biopolymers of interest, such as chitosan, has been minimal. The polymeric matrix determines the mechanical strength and chemical resistance of the final biosorbent particle. In addition, a large number of workers investigated on the role of bacteria and chitosan for the adsorption of Cr(VI). However, almost all of the reports revolve around the individual capacity of the bacteria and chitosan to remove Cr from solution. In this study, the capacity of chitosan-immobilized *A. haemolyticus*, as a new type of biosorbent, to remove Cr(VI) in batch mode was evaluated.

PREPARATION OF CHITOSAN-IMMOBILIZED
A. HAEMOLYTICUS

In this work, *A. haemolyticus* was isolated from the Cr(VI) – containing wastewater of one batek (textile-related) manufacturing premise in Kota Bharu, Kelantan. The bacterium was identified via the 16S rRNA gene-sequencing analysis from the nucleotide sequence of 597 bp. The nucleotide sequence was deposited to GenBank, where it was given accession number EF 369508 (Zakaria et al. 2007a). *A. haemolyticus* was cultivated in NB (8 g L^{-1}, Merck) at 200 rpm for 20 h and 30 °C (Certomat, B. Braun). It was then harvested via centrifugation at 7000 rpm for 5 mins and washed with sterilized deionized water. The washed cell pellets were re-suspended in 10 mL sterilized deionized water prior to autoclaving at 121 °C for 20 mins

(Hirayama, HVE-50, Japan). The bacterial cell suspension was filtered through a hydrophobic-type 0.45 μm Whatman filter-paper, and dry weight was determined after overnight drying at 60 °C.

The cell suspension was then mixed with the chitosan beads via the entrapment technique. In order to obtain the required chitosan concentration for immobilization, preliminary study on the effect of different chitosan concentrations was investigated. Chitosan solutions between 2 to 4% (w/v) were prepared by dissolving 2 to 4 g of chitosan powder (85% degree of deacetylation, Fluka) in 100 mL of 2% (v/v) acetic acid solution. Suspended cells pellets of *A. haemolyticus* were homogenized in 2% (w/v) chitosan solution (1:1) via stirring. Then, the gel beads were formed by transferring the homogenized cell pellets-chitosan solution into 1 M NaOH using a peristaltic pump at 6 mL min⁻¹. The beads were washed with deionized water and dried at 60 °C overnight. Similar procedures were repeated using 3 and 4% (w/v) chitosan solution. Control sets of experiment consist of chitosan beads without the bacteria.

Figure 4.3 shows the effect of different chitosan concentrations on the formation of biosorbent beads. Spherical beads of sufficient strength were produced using 4% (w/v) chitosan solution (Figure 4.3a). Other concentrations of chitosan solutions, i.e., 3% and 2% (w/v) (Figs. 4.3b and 4.3c, respectively) were unable to form spherical beads. Therefore, 4% (w/v) chitosan solution was used for subsequent experiments.

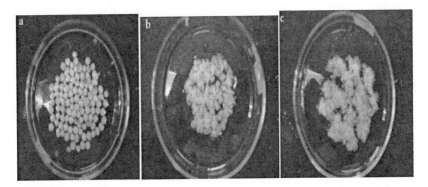

Figure 4.3. Formation of the biosorbent beads using (a) 4% (w/v) chitosan solution, (b) 3% (w/v) chitosan solution (c) 2% (w/v) chitosan solution.

EVALUATION OF CR(VI) REMOVAL
(CR, R IS LOWER CASE NOT CAPITAL R)

Effect of pH

The effect of pH on Cr(VI) removal was elucidated as follows: chitosan-immobilized *A. haemolyticus* (5 mg) or biosorbent was transferred into a series of Erlenmeyer flasks containing 25 mL of 25 mg L^{-1} Cr(VI) in deionized water. pH of the mixtures were adjusted to between 1 to 9, using either 0.1 M HCl or 0.1 M NaOH prior to shaking in an orbital shaker at 100 rpm for 24 h at room temperature. After filtration, the filtrate was determined for Cr(VI) using the diphenylcarbazide method. Similar setup minus the chitosan-immobilized *A. haemolyticus* acted as control. Stock Cr(VI) solution was prepared by dissolving 2.829 g $K_2Cr_2O_7$ (294.18 g mol^{-1}) in 1 L of deionised water. The pH of Cr(VI) solution was adjusted to 7 using 0.1 M NaOH or 0.1 M HCl before filter-sterilized using a 0.45 μm Whatman filter paper. The pH of the solution affected the removal of Cr(VI) by the biosorbent with maximum removal of 84.05 mg g^{-1} achieved at pH 3 (Figure 4.4).

Less Cr(VI), i.e., 27.5 and 30.4 mg g^{-1}, were removed at pH 2 and 4, respectively. The Cr(VI) uptake decreased tremendously above pH 7 with uptake values of less than 5 mg g^{-1}. It was also noted that most of the Cr(VI) removal action was carried out by the chitosan fraction instead of *A. haemolyticus*. This is substantiated by numerous reports where Cr(VI) removal by microorganisms-based biosorbent occurred at pH values less than 3, for example, *Agaricus bisporus* – pH 1 (Ertugay and Bayhan, 2008), *Aspergillus niger* – pH 2 (Kumar et al., 2008) and *A. haemolyticus* – pH 2 (Zakaria et al. 2007b).

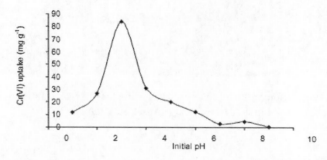

Figure 4.4. Effect of pH on Cr(VI) removal by the biosorbent (chitosan-immobilized *A. haemolyticus*).

Cr(VI) removal by chitosan, however, normally takes place at pH 3 (Ngah et al., 2006). Chitosan has a pK_a value of 6.3 to 7, thus exists mainly in the protonated forms at pH < 5 and in the neutral form at pH > 8. The amino group at the surface of chitosan beads and *A. haemolyticus* would be protonated at lower pH values. Since Cr(VI) exists in aqueous solutions in its anionic forms such as CrO_4^{2-} and $Cr_2O_7^{2-}$, its removal by the biosorbent is most likely to take place through electrostatic interaction involving the positively charged amino group and the negatively charged Cr(VI) anions (Ramnani and Sabharwal, 2006). At very low pH values, the surface of the chitosan-immobilized *A. haemolyticus* would be surrounded by the hydronium ions, which enhance Cr(VI) interaction with binding sites of the sorbent by greater attractive forces (Ngah, et al., 2006). As the pH increased, however, the overall surface charge on the sorbents becomes negative and biosorption decreases. The adsorption of Cr(VI) ions on the biosorbent beads is dependent on the stability and affinity of the Cr(VI) species. At low concentration, Cr(VI) exists mainly as $HCrO_4^-$ (pH 2 to 4), whereas the CrO_4^{2-} species becomes the main species at pH > 7. Meanwhile anions such as $Cr_2O_7^{2-}$ exist only at higher Cr(VI) concentrations. These anions can interact effectively with protonated amine functional groups.

Effect of Time

The effect of time on the Cr(VI) removal process was studied by adding 5 mg of the biosorbent into a series of 250 mL Erlenmeyer flasks containing 25 mL of 25 mg L^{-1} Cr(VI). The pH of the mixtures was then adjusted to 3 prior to shaking for 24 h. Cr(VI) removal by the biosorbent was evaluated at 0, 0.5, 1, 2, 4, 6, 12 and 24 h. The experimental setup was repeated for Cr(VI) solution only, freely suspended cells of *A. haemolyticus* and chitosan beads only which acted as control experiments, respectively. However, pH 2 was used for the freely suspended cells of *A. haemolyticus* based on the suggestion by Zakaria et al. (2007b). Profiles for the uptake of Cr(VI) by the biosorbent, chitosan beads only and free cells of *A. haemolyticus* are shown in Figure 4.5.

Each profile showed a rapid Cr(VI) uptake (indicated by a steep initial slope) until an equilibrium condition was reached, i.e., after 6 h of contact time. The chitosan-immobilized biosorbent showed the highest maximum uptake (q_e, max) value (125.9 mg g^{-1}) compared to the chitosan beads (74.2 mg g^{-1}) and free cells of *A. haemolyticus* (37.4 mg g^{-1}). Similar conditions were reported by Ngah et al. (2006), Baran et al. (2006) and Kumar et al., (2008).

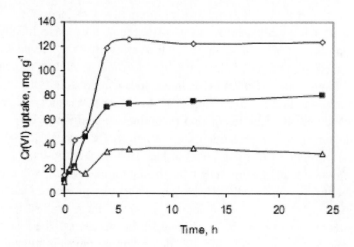

Figure 4.5. Cr(VI) uptake at different contact time; ◊ – biosorbent, ■ – chitosan beads only, Δ – free cells of *A. haemolyticus*.

It was also reported that the Cr(VI) uptake decreased gradually as the initially large number of vacant surface binding sites is now occupied, while the remaining sites may be difficult to occupy due to repulsive forces between the solute molecules of the solid and bulk phase (Kumar et al., 2008). It is also worthy to note that in this study, a longer time (6 h) was needed for *A. haemolyticus* to reach equilibrium compared to other reported biosorbents (Table 4.1). This was due to the much lower amount of biosorbent used, i.e., 5 mg compared to the much higher dosage for the other biosorbents.

**Table 4.1. Time to reach equilibrium for the removal of Cr(VI) by
different biosorbents**

Biosorbent	Equilibrium time	Reference
A. niger	1 h	Kumar et al., 2008
Bacillus thuringiensis	0.25 h	Sahin and Ozturk, 2005
Pseudomonas sp.	1.5 h	Ziagova et al., 2007
Pinus sylvestris	2 h	Ucun et al., 2002
Chitosan-immobilized *A .haemolyticus*	6 h	This study

Effect of Biosorbent Dosage and Cr(VI) Concentration

For the biosorbent dosage experiments, three different biosorbent concentrations, namely, 5, 10 and 15 mg, were added into 25 mL of 25 and 300 mg L^{-1} Cr(VI) solutions at pH 3. The mixtures were shaken for 6 h prior to Cr(VI) determination. To assess the capacity of the biosorbent to remove different concentrations of Cr(VI), a series of Erlenmeyer flasks containing 25 mL Cr(VI) solutions ranging from 25 to 300 mg L^{-1} were prepared. The pH was adjusted to 3. Then, 5 mg of the biosorbent was added into each flask, followed by shaking at 100 rpm for 6 h. Cr(VI) solutions without biosorbent acted as control. Highest Cr(VI) uptake of 238.5 mg g^{-1} was achieved when 5 mg of the biosorbent was contacted with 300 mg L^{-1} Cr(VI). Overall Cr(VI) uptake by the biosorbent showed a decreasing trend with the increase in biosorbent dosage (Figure 4.6). This condition can be attributed to the electrostatic interactions between cells, where available binding sites such as amine and amino groups were protected from occupation by Cr(VI) (Ziagova et al., 2007; Sekhar et al., 1998; Bera et al., 2006). This is evident from this study where the use of 15 mg biosorbent resulted in a Cr(VI) uptake that was 10 times lower than that by 5 mg of biosorbent.

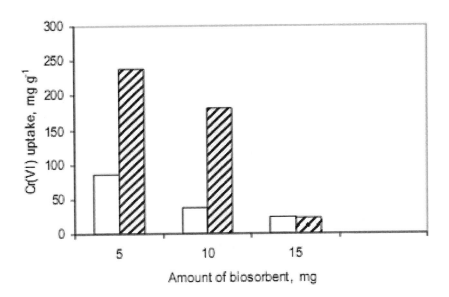

Figure 4.6. Cr(VI) uptake by 5, 10 and 15 mg of biosorbent at □ – 25 mg L^{-1} Cr(VI) and ■ - 300 mg L^{-1} Cr(VI).

However, the opposite trend was observed when the concentrations of Cr(VI) were varied. A gradual increase in Cr(VI) uptake was observed with values of 120 mg g^{-1} at 25 mg L^{-1} Cr(VI), 162 mg g^{-1} at 50 mg L^{-1}, 235 mg g^{-1} (75 mg L^{-1}), 238.2 mg g^{-1} (150 mg L^{-1}) and 250.4 mg g^{-1} at 300 mg L^{-1}. A similar situation such as this where maximum Cr(VI) uptake (q_e, max) achieved at the highest Cr(VI) concentration used has also been reported by Anjana et al. (2007), Tewari et al. (2005), Ziagova et al. (2007) and Kumar et al. (2008). This condition was due to the presence of higher amounts of free Cr(VI) ions in the solution to be adsorped by the biosorbent. Moreover, higher Cr(VI) concentration would provide increased driving force to overcome all mass transfer resistance of metal ions between the aqueous and solid phases resulting in higher probability of collision between Cr(VI) ions and sorbents (Tewari et al., 2005). In addition, increasing metal ions concentration increased the number of collisions between metal ions and sorbent, which enhanced the sorption process (Bai and Abraham, 2003).

For the desorption studies, 5 mg of the biosorbent was contacted (6 h, 100 rpm) with 25 mL of 300 mg L^{-1} Cr(VI) solution at pH 3 in a series of 250 mL Erlenmeyer flasks. Upon filtration at the end of the contact time, the biosorbent was collected and washed using deionized water to remove excess Cr(VI). Then, the Cr(VI) adsorped by the biosorbents was desorped using 25 mL of either 0.1 to 10 mM EDTA, H$_2$SO$_4$ or HNO$_3$. The mixtures were contacted for one hour where the percentage of Cr(VI) desorbed was determined as shown in Equation 4.1:

$$\text{Percentage of desorption} = \frac{\text{Cr(VI) desorped (mg L}^{-1})}{\text{Cr(VI) adsorped (mg L}^{-1})} \times 100 \qquad \text{(Equation 4.1)}$$

During the desorption study, H$_2$SO$_4$ displayed the highest ability to desorp Cr(VI) from the biosorbent compared to EDTA and HNO$_3$. Maximum Cr(VI) desorption was achieved using 10 mM of the desorbing agents with maximum removal percentages of 72.3% for H$_2$SO$_4$, 47.3% - EDTA and 21.5% - HNO$_3$. The better performance of H$_2$SO$_4$ to desorp Cr(VI) was due to it being a diprotic acid and a stronger acid than both HNO$_3$ and EDTA. EDTA is a hexadentate chelating agent and is capable of forming a complex with Cr(VI) ions much in the mould of a cation exchanger.

The Cr(VI) reduction study from an actual industrial wastewater was carried out using wastewater obtained from the rinse-bath tank of a local electroplating company in Masai, Johor. Some characteristics of the wastewater are as follows: colour – yellow to dark orange, turbidity – clear, pH – 2.54 ± 0.05, no microbiological count recorded and Cr(VI) of 275 mg L^{-1}. Two parameters were looked into, namely, pH and multiple biosorption-desorption cycles. For the effect of pH study, 5 mg of the biosorbent was added into two 250 mL conical flasks containing 25 mL of the electroplating wastewater. The pH of one of the flask was adjusted to 3, while pH of the other flask was left unadjusted, i.e., 2.54. The mixtures were then shaken at 100 rpm for 6 h. Cr(VI) uptake by the biosorbent was determined from the filtrate obtained at the end of the experiment. Flask containing electroplating waste only, without the biosorbent, was used as control. Similar experimental setup was used during the multiple biosorption-desorption cycles study. After the 6 h contact time, the biosorbent was separated from the solution and was contacted with 10 mM H_2SO_4 to remove the adsorped Cr(VI) from the biosorbent. Then, the biosorbent was rinsed using deionized water to remove excess H_2SO_4. The biosorption-desorption cycles were repeated for three times using the same Cr(VI) solution and biosorbent.

When Cr(VI) removal from the actual industrial wastewater was investigated, pH of the wastewater was adjusted to 3.0, i.e., the pre-determined optimum pH for Cr(VI) removal. However, this does not result in a significant increase in Cr(VI) removal with a q_{max} value of 254.52 mg g^{-1} compared to q_{max} at the original pH of 2.54, i.e., 278.34 mg g^{-1}. This represents a Cr(VI) removal percentage of 40% for the pH-adjusted electroplating wastewater compared to 43.3% for the original electroplating wastewater. This finding is very significant as it shows that the biosorbent has the ability to remove Cr(VI) from the electroplating wastewater without the need for pH adjustment, hence it can minimize the overall operating expenditures for the Cr(VI) removal process. From the multiple biosorption-desorption cycles study, the Cr(VI) uptake capacity of the biosorbent was unaltered after three cycles with uptake values of more than 200 mg g^{-1} (Figure 4.7). However, the biosorbent's Cr(VI) uptake capacity decreased to 84 mg g^{-1} after the fourth cycle. This was due to the incomplete desorption of the Cr(VI) anions from the surface of the biosorbent. The presence of this irreversibly bound Cr(VI) at the surface of the biosorbent would limit the number of available and active binding sites, hence hindering maximum removal of Cr(VI) ions from the electroplating wastewater.

The initial and residual concentration of Cr(VI) was determined colorimetrically at 540 nm using the diphenyl carbazide (DPC) method with a detection limit of 5 µg L^{-1}.

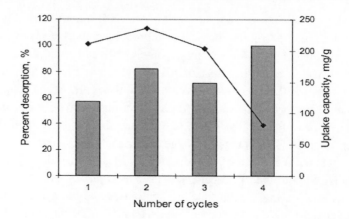

Figure 4.7. Cr(VI) uptake and desorption profiles using 10 mM H2SO4; ■ -% Cr(VI) desorption, ♦ – Cr(VI) uptake capacity.

The Langmuir and Freundlich adsorption isotherms were used to evaluate the biosorption capacity of the chitosan-immobilized *A. haemolyticus* (biosorbent). The Langmuir and Freundlich equations are as described in Equations 4.2 to 4.5, respectively:

$$q_e = \frac{Q^{o}bC_e}{1+bC_e} \text{ (Nonlinear form)} \qquad \text{(Equation 4.2)}$$

$$\frac{C_e}{q_e} = \frac{1}{Q^{o}b} + \frac{1}{Q^{o}}C_e \text{ (Linear form)} \qquad \text{(Equation 4.3)}$$

where q_e is the amount of solute adsorbed per unit weight of adsorbent (mg g^{-1}), C_e is the equilibrium concentration of solute in the bulk solution (mg L^{-1}), Q^{o} is the monolayer adsorption capacity (mg g^{-1}) and b is the constant related to the free adsorption energy. b is the reciprocal of the concentration at which half saturation of the adsorbent is reached.

$$q_e = K_F C_e^{1/n} \text{ (non-linear form)} \qquad \text{(Equation 4.4)}$$

$$\ln q_e = \ln K_F + \frac{1}{n}\ln C_e \text{ (linear form)} \qquad \text{(Equation 4.5)}$$

where q_e is the amount of solute adsorbed per unit weight of adsorbent (mg g^{-1}), C_e is the equilibrium concentration of solute in the bulk solution (mg L^{-1}), K_F is a constant indicative of the relative adsorption capacity of the adsorbent (mg g^{-1}), and the constant $1/n$ indicates the intensity of the adsorption.

ELECTRON MICROSCOPY STUDY

For the Electron Microscopy study, a small amount of the desiccator-dried biosorbent was mounted on a sample holder and coated with gold (15 to 20 nm) before viewing under the electron microscope (Philips SEM XL 40). Sample for the Transmission Electron Microscopy (TEM) analysis was prepared using the modified method of Bencosme and Tsutsumi (1970) as follows: the bisorbent was fixed with 3% (v/v) glutaraldehyde in 0.1 M phosphate buffer saline for at least 30 mins. It was then washed and suspended in 5 mL of the same buffer followed by staining using 1% (v/v) osmium tetraoxide in deionized water for 20 mins. After washing in three changes of deionized water, the sample was stained using 2% (v/v) uranyl acetate in deionized water for 10 mins. It was then rinsed in deionized water prior to dehydration in 50% (3 mins), 70% (3 mins), 90% (3 mins) and 100% (v/v) ethanol (3 mins). The dehydrated sample was added with two changes of propylene oxide for 5 mins each. Prior to embedment in epoxy, the samples were infiltrated firstly in 1:1 mixture of epoxy and propylene oxide for 15 mins, followed by another 15 mins in 3:1 mixture of epoxy and propylene oxide and finally in pure resin for 10 mins. The sample was then embedded in a fresh epoxy resin and polymerized at 75 °C (45 mins) and 95 °C (45 mins). The resultant resin block containing bacterial sample was allowed to cool at room temperature overnight before ultra-thin sectioning (70 to 80 nm thick) using LKB-IV Systems 2128 (Bromma, Sweden) ultramicrotome. The ultra-thin sections obtained were then viewed using TEM.

From the FESEM analysis, the biosorbents appear as having a rough surface area and a porous internal structure (Figures 4.8a and 4.8b). There is no significant difference between the chitosan beads and the chitosan-immobilized *A. haemolyticus* except for the porosity of the biosorbent beads. The less porosity feature of the chitosan-immobilized *A. haemolyticus* may indicate the colonization of the biosorbent beads by the bacterial cells.

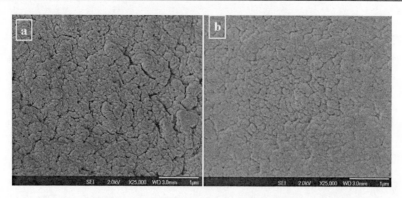

Figure 4.8. Micrographs of (a) chitosan beads (b) *A. haemolyticus* immobilized in chitosan; bar represents 1 μm.

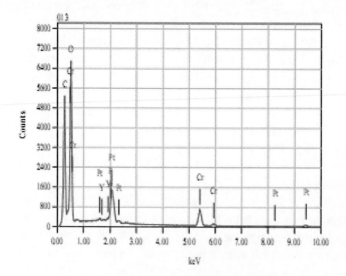

Figure 4.9. EDAX analysis of Cr(VI) uptake by *A. haemolyticus* immobilized in chitosan.

EDAX analysis showed the presence of Cr on the surface of the biosorbent, hence supporting the role of the biosorbent to remove Cr(VI) from solution (Figure 4.9). TEM was carried out to ascertain the location of Cr(VI) deposition inside the beads. However, upon sectioning of the resin using an ultramicrotome, the thin sections cannot be obtained due to the interaction between resin and chitosan. Hence, no conclusive remark can be made.

CONCLUSION

Chitosan-immobilized *A. haemolyticus* showed a much higher Cr(VI) uptake compared to chitosan only or cells of *A. haemolyticus* only. Adsorped Cr(VI) can also be removed easily using diluted acid solutions. This indicates the potential of using this kind of biosorbent as an alternative technology to sequester Cr(VI) from aqueous environment such as industrial wastewater.

ACKNOWLEDGMENT

The authors would like to acknowledge the Ministry of Science, Technology and Innovation, Malaysia for funding the project via the E-ScienceFund. Thanks also to Jefri bin Samin and Dr.Rafiq for the FESEM work (Material Science Lab. Mechanical Eng., Universiti Teknologi Malaysia).

REFERENCES

Ahluwalia, S.S. and Goyal, D. (2006). Microbial and Plant Derived Biomass for Removal of Heavy Metals from Wastewater. *Bioresource Technology.* 98, 2243–2257.

Anjana, K., Kaushik, A., Kiran, B. and Nisha, R. (2007). Biosorption of Cr(VI) by Immobilized Biomass of Two Indigenous Strains of Cyanobacteria Isolated from Metal Contaminated Soil. *Journal of Hazardous Materials.* 148, 383–386.

Arica, M.Y and Bayramoglu, G. (2005). Cr(VI) Biosorption from Aqueous Solutions using Free and Immobilized Biomass of Lentinus Sajor-caju: Preparation and Kinetic Characterization. *Colloids and Surfaces.* 253, 203-211.

Aziz, H.A., Adlan,. M.N. and Ariffin,.K.S. (2007). Heavy Metals (Cd, Pb, Zn, Ni, Cu and Cr(III)) Removal from Water in Malaysia: Post Treatment by High Quality Limestone. *Bioresource Technology.* 99: 1578-1583.

Babel, S. and Kurniawan, T.A. (2003). A Review of Low Cost Adsorbents for Heavy Metals Uptake from Contaminated Waste. *Journal of Hazardous Materials.* B97, 219–243.

Bai, R.S. and Abraham, T.E. (2003). Studies on Chromium (VI) Adsorption–Desorption using Immobilized Fungal Biomass. *Bioresource Technology.* 87, 17-26.

Bailey, S.E., Olin, T.J., Bricka, R.M. and Adrian, D. (1999). A Review of Potentially Low-Cost Sorbents for Heavy Metals. *Water Research.* 33, 2469-2479.

Baran, A., Bıcak, E., Baysal, S. H. and Onal, S. (2006). Comparative Studies on the Adsorption of Cr(VI) Ions on to Various Sorbents. *Bioresource Technology.* 98, 661–665.

Bera, D., Chattopadhyay, P. and Ray, L. (2006). Chromium(VI) Biosorption by Immobilized Biomass of *Bacillus Cereus* M116. *Journal for Hazardous Substance Research.* 6, 1-23.

Boddu, V.M., Abburi, K., Talbott, J.L. and Smith, E.D. (2003). Removal of Hexavalent Chromium from Wastewater using a New Composite Chitosan Biosorbent. *Environ. Sci. Technol.* 37, 4449-4456

Cardenas, G., Orlando, P. and Edelio, T. (2001). Synthesis and Applications of Chitosan Mercaptanes as Heavy Metal Retention Agent. International *Journal of Biological Macromolecules.* 28, 167–174.

Dacera, D.D.M. and Babel, S. (2007). Removal of Heavy Metals from Contaminated Sewage Sludge using *Aspergillus Niger* Fermented Raw Liquid from Pineapple Wastes. *Bioresource Technology.* 99, 1682-1689.

Ertugay, N. and Bayhan, Y.K. (2008). Biosorption of Cr(VI) from Aqueous Solutions by Biomass of Agaricus bisporus. *Journal of Hazardous Materials.* 154, 432–439.

Kumar, R., Bishnoi, N. R. and Garima and Bishnoi, K. (2008). Biosorption of Chromium(VI) from Aqueous Solution and Electroplating Wastewater using Fungal Biomass. *Chemical Engineering Journal.* 135, 202–208.

Lee, S.T., Mi, F.L., Shen, Y.J. and Shyu, S.S. (2001). Equilibrium and Kinetic Studies of Copper (II) Ion Uptake by Chitosan-Tripolyphosphate Chelating Resin. *Polymer.* .42. 1879–1892

Namasivayam, C. and Sureshkumar, M.V. (2008). Removal of Chromium(VI) from Water and Wastewater Using Surfactant Modified Coconut Coir Pith as a Biosorbent. *Bioresource Technology.* 99, 2218-2225.

Ngah, W. S. W., Kamari, A., Fatinathan, S. and Ng, P. W. (2006). Adsorption of Chromium from Aqueous Solution using Chitosan Beads. *Adsorption.* 12, 249–257.

Onal, S., Baysal, S. H. and Ozdemir, G. (2007). Studies on The Applicability of Alginate-Entrapped *Chryseomonas luteola* TEM 05 for heavy metal biosorption. *Journal of Hazardous Materials.* 146, 417–420.

Ramnani, S. P. and Sabharwal, S. (2006). Adsorption Behavior of Cr(VI) onto Radiation Crosslinked Chitosan and its Possible Application for the Treatment of Wastewater Containing Cr(VI). *Reactive and Functional Polymers.* 66, 902–909.

Sahin, Y. and Ozturk, A. (2005). Biosorption of Chromium(VI) Ions from Aqueous Solution by The Bacterium *Bacillus Thuringiensis*. *Process Biochemistry.* 40, 1895–1901.

Sekhar, K.C., Subramanian, S., Modak, J.M., Natarajan, K.A. (1998). Removal of Metal Ions Using an Industrial Biomass With Reference to Environmental Control. International *Journal of Mineral Processing.* 53, 107–120.

Tewari, N, Vasudevan, P. and Guha, K. (2005). Study on biosorption of Cr(VI) by Mucor hiemalis. *Biochemical Engineering Journal.* 23, 185–192.

Ucun, H.Y., Bayhan, K., Kaya, Y., Cakici, A.O. and Algur, F. (2002). Biosorption of Chromium(VI) from Aqueous Solution by Cone Biomass of Pinus Sylvestris. *Bioresource Technology.* 85, 155–158.

Zakaria, Z.A., Zakaria, Z., Surif, S. and Ahmad, W.A. (2007a). Hexavalent Chromium Reduction by *Acinetobacter Haemolyticus* Isolated from Heavy-Metal Contaminated Wastewater. *Journal of Hazardous Materials.* 146, 30–38.

Zakaria, Z. A., Aruleswaran, N., Kaur, S. and Ahmad, W.A. (2007b). Biosorption and Bioreduction of Cr(VI) by Locally Isolated Cr-resistant Bacteria. *Water Science and Technology.* 56(8), 117–123.

Ziagova, M., Dimitriadis, G., Aslanidou, D., Papaioannou, X., Tzannetaki E. L, M. and Kyriakides, L. (2007). Comparative Study of Cd(II) and Cr(VI) Biosorption on *Staphylococcus xylosus* and *Pseudomonas sp.* in Single and Binary Mixtures. *Bioresource Technology.* 98, 2859–2865.

In: Bacteria in Environmental Biotechnology   ISBN 978-1-61728-350-5
Editor: W. A. Ahmad et al.   © 2011 Nova Science Publishers, Inc.

Chapter 5

PRODUCTION OF PROTEIN LIQUOR BY MICROBIAL FERMENTATION OF PRAWN WASTE

Nurzahwani Mohd Noor, Zainoha Zakaria,
Madihah Md Salleh
and Muhammed Suhaimee Abd Manaf

ABSTRACT

Aquaculture sector is highly dependent on adequate supply of cheap and nutritional feedstuffs. Locally, dependency on expensive imported proteinaceous raw materials is a major constraint for aquaculture development. In this chapter, the potential of fermented prawn waste (*Penaeus monodon*) silage as an alternative protein source is reported. Bacterial fermentation of prawn waste at 37 °C using glucose as substrate for three days resulted in a protein liquor or silage containing high protein (47%) and low fibre (0.8%) contents, which fits the requirement for a good ingredient in an aquaculture fish diet. In addition, prawn waste silage remains stable at acid condition (pH 4) up to 60 days. The fermentation can also be carried out at ambient temperature. The probiotic rich silage is also advantageous for fish gut health. Another advantage to this process is the valuable by-product, i.e., chitin, which is a biomaterial with great potentials for commercial applications.

INTRODUCTION

Nutrition and feeding strategies play a central and essential role in the development of an aquaculture sector. At present, commercial diets are the most commonly used diets for aquaculture purposes to maintain fish health and growth. However, development of aquaculture sector is hampered by inadequate supply of cheap and nutritional feedstuffs, in particular, the protein source. Demand for fish diet raw materials is expected to increase in the near future as aquaculture industry has been identified as one of the potential sector to be expanded especially in Malaysia (Malaysian Fisheries Department, 2004). Since major items such as maize, rice bran, meat meal, and fishmeal are imported, dependency on these expensive imported materials is viewed as one of the major constraints for aquaculture augmentation (Food and Agriculture Organization, 2007).

One of the potential sources of protein is prawn waste produced by the prawn processing industries, whereby the prawn waste contains 35 to 55% of calcium, 15 to 40% of protein and 14 to 30% of chitin (Ornum, 1992; Legaretta et al., 1996). At present, this waste product contributes to the production of chitin through chemical processes at extreme pH and temperature. Chitin, which was discovered by Braconot in 1821, is now a well-manufactured and commercialized product since the 1970s (Brzeski, 1987). However, this chemical method generates a large volume of aqueous waste as well as discarding many useful components including the precious protein (Brzeski, 1987; Zakaria et al., 1998). In order to overcome the environmental problems as well as to recover the valuable protein, a biotechnological approach has been developed on the treatment of prawn waste using lactic acid fermentation. The fermentation involving lactic acid bacteria is seen to be promising, with advantages such as protein recovery and reduced chemical consumption (Zakaria et al., 1998). It is interesting to note that the liquor produced through the fermentation process is rich in protein and can be utilized as an ingredient for animal feed (Hall and Silva, 1992).

In addition, the fermentation method can also be adopted by the small-scale industries as fermentation is generally accepted as a safe and low-cost process (Soomro et al., 2002). From an economic point of view, the production of nutritional protein locally will relieve the local aquaculture industries from the use of expensive imported protein meal. The problem of using local protein ingredient is not the lack of resources, but how to get it as nutritious as imported ones and at a cheaper price. At present, there have been practices among the small-scale aquaculture industry to incorporate whole prawn waste as feed meal, in an effort to save cost of preparing fish feed diets. The prawn waste is sun dried and ground before it could be used as fish diet. However, there are disadvantages of using dried prawn waste meal such as its high fibre and chitin content, and, with an unhygienic preparation, it might lead to a feed meal with low protein content and high microbial loading (Meyers, 1986). The alternative method of using lactic acid fermentation on prawn waste is gaining interest worldwide, as the process and its products are safe and cheap. Nwanna (2003) reported that the liquid portion obtained from the fermentation of Nigerian prawn head for 14 days using 15% of cane molasses and 5% of lactic acid bacterium culture was suitable as an ingredient in feeds for African Catfish, *Clarias gariepinus*. The high protein and amino acid profile in the liquor were comparable to the usual fishmeal. Although it was evident that the research in Nigeria had been successful, the process variable needs to be improved in order to be applied in Malaysia using available raw material. A similar study by Zakaria et al. (1998) has shown that more than 90% of protein from the prawn waste could be recovered within a shorter period of only 72 h. Shirai et al. (2001) also concluded that the best result in fermentation of prawn waste was obtained after a fermentation process of 72 days using 10% of carbon source (glucose) and 5% of cells inoculum. As variation in the prawn wastes contents would be encountered due to the handling and processing methods, a new formulation of fish feed involving our own tropical prawn waste needs to be studied.

BACTERIA AND PRAWN WASTE

Lactic acid bacteria (LAB) used in the fermentation process was isolated from fermented tiger prawn (*Penaeus monodon*) waste (Hamizatul, 2000). It was identified as *Lactobacillus casei* and grown in the MRS broth (De Man, Rogosa and Sharpe) with glucose monohydrate used as a carbon and energy source. The bacteria were kept at − 80 °C in MRS broth supplemented with 15% glycerol (v/v) until further use. To prepare the inoculum, the stock LAB culture was incubated in MRS broth at 37 °C for 24 h followed by sub-culturing into a fresh MRS broth (2%, v/v). The frozen tiger prawn waste (*Penaeus monodon*) was obtained from one seafood processing factory in Pasir Gudang, Johor. The prawn waste consists of all components other than the meat, which include the heads, exoskeleton, and tail section. The head portion may contain some meat as well as the enzyme-rich guts. During transportation, the prawn waste was covered with ice in an insulated box to inhibit the autolysis process. The waste was minced through a 4.5 mm die plate using an industrial mincer (Rheninghaus Meat Mincer, model EVE/ALL 22, Italy) and was stored in 1 kg portions in plastic bags at − 20 °C until further use.

FERMENTATION OF PRAWN WASTE

Glucose, Lactic Acid Content and Proximate Analysis

The prawn waste fermentation process was carried out in two batches for two purposes. The first purpose was to monitor the stability of the fermentation products as well as the overall 60-day fermentation process. This should provide useful insights for any potential on-site application, which normally involves long durations due to transportation and handling problems. The second purpose of the fermentation was to optimize the protein production and was carried out in three days only. All experiments were performed in duplicate.

The elucidation on the stability of the fermented prawn waste products was carried out using a mixture of 1.0 kg thawed minced prawn waste, 10% (w/w) glucose monohydrate and 10% (v/v) inoculum of the LAB bacteria. The fermentation was carried out in a covered 2 L beaker and incubated at 37 °C for 60 days. Stirring was occasionally provided, especially during the first 24 h, in order to make the fermentation mixture homogeneous and prevent spoilage at the top of the mixture. At various time intervals, 10 mL of the fermented prawn waste was determined for pH and protein content using the Kjeldahl method (Zakaria et al., 1998). Similar experimental setup was used to determine the amount of protein produced during the fermentation process but the time was extended to 72 h. The following parameters were monitored: bacterial growth, pH, glucose and lactic acid contents. Upon completion of the fermentation process, the fermented slurry was filtered through a coarse cloth to separate the solid from the liquid part. Weights of both the solid and liquid parts were determined to ascertain the extent of recovery after the fermentation process. The solid part was dried at 100 °C and analyzed for total nitrogen, chitin, crude protein, ash, and moisture contents (AOAC, 1980). Similar experimental parameters were used during the study on the effect of temperature on the production of lactic acid by the bacteria at 37 °C and ambient room temperature.

Glucose concentration was determined using the dinitrosalicylic acid (DNS) test (Chaplin and Kennedy, 1986). Concentration of lactic acid was determined using the HPLC system (Waters 600, Millford, MA) fitted with UV detector (Waters 2489, Millford, MA). An aliquot of 3 mL or approximately equivalent with 3 g of the fermented slurry was mixed with distilled water (1:10) and centrifuged (Kubota, Japan) at 10,000 g for 15 min. The supernatant was filtered through a 0.45 and 0.20 μm cellulose acetate membrane. The filtrate (20 μL) was injected into an ion exclusion organic acids column (Aminex HPX - 87H, Biorad, Hercules), which was eluted with 5 mM of H_2SO_4. The systems were operated at ambient temperature with a flow rate of 0.6 mL min^{-1}. The following methods were used during the proximate analysis: protein (Kjeldahl Method), chitin (Kjeldahl Method using acidified or alkali-treated samples), and crude fat (solvent method using Soctex System HT6 TECATOR). Crude fibre, ash and moisture content were determined using the typical procedures as outlined by AOAC (1980).

The fermentation process changes the prawn waste from its original semi-solid condition to that of dilute slurry, particularly during the first 24 h. A black layer was formed at the top of fermentation mixture after 6 to 10 h of fermentation. Occasional stirring was provided to ensure good mixing, which is important to avoid the growth of undesirable microflora. However, the stirring process was carried out very slowly in order to avoid excessive loss of CO_2, which is crucial for the growth of lactic acid bacteria (Jay, 1992). Moreover, excessive stirring will thicken the liquor, which is caused by the formation of stable foam from the "whipping up" of protein present in the fermentation liquor. If this condition occurred, the insoluble chitin sediment would be difficult to separate from the brownish, viscous liquor. During the first three days of fermentation, the pH value decreased sharply from pH 7.5 to 4.0, indicating good fermentation of silage. This pH value is within the recommended value for successful silage fermentation (Shahidi and Synowiecki, 1991).

In the excess sugar and limited access to oxygen conditions, glucose was fermented by LAB via the Embden-Meyerhoff pathway to produce lactic acid and consecutively lowered the pH (Madigan et al., 1997; Axelsson, 1993). The production of acid had a dual effect on the substrate. Firstly, the preservation of prawn waste at a low pH condition and the dissolution of $CaCO_3$ producing copious amounts of CO_2. This helps explain the appearance of gas bubbles at the top layer of the fermented prawn waste during the early stage and after 24 h of fermentation time. The acidic condition is also an added advantage to the process for chitin recovery, as it promotes the enzymes to break down the protein from the prawn waste, forming a protein rich-liquor, thus purifying the chitin fraction (Hall and Silva, 1992; Fagbenro, 1996).

Throughout the fermentation process, the pH remains stable at 3.9 to 4.1. Fagbenro (1996) obtained similar results during a 30-day fermentation of prawn head at 30 °C, using 5% (w/w) *Lactobacillus plantarum* as inoculum and 15% (w/w) cane molasses as the carbohydrate source. The pH stability might be due to the buffering actions of amino acids and Ca present in the prawn waste. These amino acids and Ca have been reported to be present at 51 and 24% (w/w), respectively (Shirai et al., 2001). It can then be concluded that this process is suitable to be used for long durations whereby the fermentation products remain in stable conditions for up to 60 days. The protein content rose sharply from 2.5 ± 0.1% to 50.0 ± 1.7% after three days, and gradually increased to 56.0 ± 2.5% after seven days (Figure 5.1). Thereafter, the protein percentage slightly increased from 57.0 ± 2.6% on day 14, to 59.0 ± 2.2% on day 60 of incubation.

The protein liquor was produced from the autolytic process. During fermentation, the acidic environment allowed the endogenous enzymes to perform the autolysis process and protein breakdown from the prawn waste (Hall and Silva, 1992). The enzymes involved were mainly the proteolytic enzymes produced by *Lactobacillus*, the gut bacteria present in the intestinal system of the prawn or the proteases present in the biowaste (Wood, 1998). At the same time, the acid conditions dissolve $CaCO_3$, which is analogous to the demineralisation step in the traditional chitin recovery process (Simpson et al., 1994).

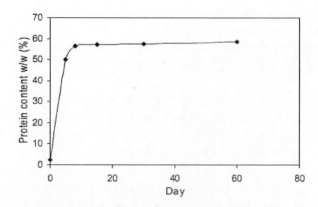

Figure 5.1. Protein content (dry weight basis) of the protein liquor during 60 days of fermentation by LAB.

Thus, the lactic acid fermentation produced liquor with a high content of soluble peptides and free amino acid as well as partially purified chitin (Hall and Silva, 1992; Wood, 1998). Hence, this explained how the protein percentage increased to 50.0 ± 1.7% after three days of fermentation (Figure 5.2). Even though the protein content in the protein liquor increased from 50.01 ± 1.7% on the third day to 56.4 ± 2.5% on the seventh day, the impact may be negligible in terms of industrial application. The four days needed to have an increase of 6% of the protein yield may not be that attractive to the industrial sector. Shirai et al. (2001) reported that the best time for fermentation of prawn waste was three days, while Zakaria et al. (1998) also reported that most of the protein in the prawn waste could be recovered after three days of LAB fermentation. Based on the result, a three-day process was chosen as the appropriate time for the protein production in the subsequent studies. This study also demonstrated that the fermentation of prawn waste can be left for a period of 60 days without any spoilage taking place. This is extremely advantageous for industrial application point of view as especially when there are not enough facilities are available to immediately convert the protein liquor into feeds.

The relationship between glucose consumption and lactic acid generation is shown in Figure 5.2. Highest glucose consumption by the bacteria occurs between 12 to 48 h, where the glucose concentration decreased sharply from 115.9 to 12.0 mg mL^{-1}. Complete glucose consumption was recorded after 72 h of bacterial growth.

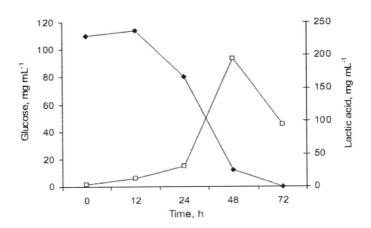

Figure 5.2. Profiles for glucose consumption (◆) and lactic acid production (▢) during the fermentation of prawn waste by LAB.

The direct influence of the amount of sugar presence on the fermentation process has been well documented (Hassan and Health, 1986; Wyk and Heydenrych, 1985). The presence of excessive amounts of glucose would lead to a prolonged lag phase and the possibility of putrefaction (Shirai et al., 2001). From this study, the addition of 10% v/v of glucose was proven sufficient for a fermentation period of 72 h, based on the absence of spoilage signs and the low pH recorded throughout the fermentation process, which is indicative of the production of lactic acid. Although a lower dose of glucose (5% v/v) has been reported by other researchers (Rao et al., 2002), the attractiveness of the process was offset by the need to maintain the pH at 6.0 throughout the fermentation process. The lactic acid concentration in the liquor increases from 9.6 to 197.6 mg mL^{-1} after 48 h of fermentation. The lactic acid produced through the fermentation process is an added advantage to the chitin recovery, as it was used in the demineralization process. In the solution, lactic acid reacts with $CaCO_3$ component in the chitin fraction, leading to the formation of calcium lactate. Lactic acid is normally used as a food preservative in animal and vegetable products. In this study, the *in-situ* production of lactic acid helps to preserve the prawn waste byinhibiting the growth of pathogenic bacteria. Furthermore, the use of lactic acid bacteria in the fermentation process is regarded as a natural and safe process as well as representing a low cost method of preservation.

Results from the analysis of the crude fibre content (%) in the initial waste and the protein liquor suggested that protein liquor with low fibre content was obtained, as the fibres that come mainly from the chitin component of the prawn waste, had been removed from the protein liquor. The final fibre content in the protein liquor was only $0.8 \pm 0.2\%$, which translates into a fibre removal percentage of 99.2% (initial fibre content of $21.5 \pm 0.1\%$). The low fibre content in the protein liquor enhances its application in animal feed formulation compared to the dried shrimp waste, which is used in the broilers diet with a fibre content of 12.3% (Fanimo, 2000).

The results proved that the fermentation of prawn waste with LAB can be carried out at both 37 °C and at ambient temperature (27 to 33 °C) (Figure 5.3). Fermentation at 37 °C was optimum for the growth of LAB (Hamizatul, 2000). Normally, lactic acid fermentation can be carried out at 5 to 45 °C, depending on the type of LAB used. Nwanna (2003) also reported successful fermentation carried out at ambient temperature. Having a process operating at ambient temperature is an advantage, especially to the small-scale industry.

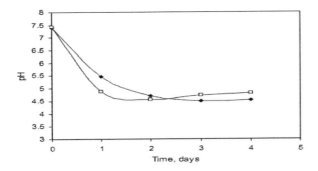

Figure 5.3. Fermentation of shrimp waste by LAB at 37 °C (□) and at ambient temperature (◆) .

In Malaysia, many traditional fermentation-based food industries, such as tapai, budu and cencaluk, are carried out at ambient temperature. As far as the fermentation process is concerned, having an acidic condition is vital to avoid putrefactions and spoilage (Jay, 1992).

PROTEIN RECOVERY FROM PROTEIN LIQUOR

The protein recovery was carried out after the fermentation process was completed. The whole fermentation product is designated as "silage." Further separation of the silage would yield two fractions, namely, the insoluble chitin solids or the "sediment," and the liquid fraction, which is referred to as the "liquor." The weight and moisture contents of the fermentation components are shown in Table 5.1.

Table 5.1. The weight and moisture contents of the fermentation components

Components	Initial waste	Silage	Liquor (Protein)	Sediment (Chitin)
Weight (g); (wet basis)	1200 ± 4.6	1147 ± 4	850 ± 2.4	187 ± 3.7
% Moisture content	83.7 ± 0.9	n.d	92.9 ± 0.1	67.4 ± 0.7

n.d: not determined.

Table 5.2. Proximate analysis on the initial waste, liquor and sediment (chitin fraction) after 72 h of fermentation

Fraction	Protein (%)	Chitin (%)
Initial waste (%)	42.6 ± 1.2	22.5 ± 0.2
(g, wet basis)	510.7 ± 0.1	270 ± 0.01
Liquor (%)	47.3 ± 1.1	6.5 ± 0.2
(g, wet basis)	402.1 ± 9.6	55.3 ± 1.4
Sediment (%)	15.0 ± 0.1	74.0 ± 6.1
(g, wet basis)	28.05 ± 0.2	138.4 ± 11.4

At the end of the fermentation process, proximate analysis was carried out on the protein liquor and the sediment (Table 5.2). Overall, 78% protein was recovered in the liquor. Only 6.5% of chitin was left in the protein liquor, whereas 28 g of the initial 511 g protein in the initial waste was still bonded to the chitin fraction. For large-scale application of the process, the percentage of protein recovery can be increased using more sophisticated equipment during the product collection and the separation process. Attempts were made to convert the protein liquor into the powdered form for ease of handling and also to improve the protein content. However, this process did not achieve the desired objective and hence, the protein liquor is best applied in the form of viscous liquor or silage. Raa (1980) had stated that fish silage production, either through acid treatment or fermentation process, is one of the less capital intensive compared to the other storage methods, and is feasible in both the small and large-scale industries.

Crude protein content in the protein liquor was determined as 47.3%. This value is lower than the imported fishmeal, which is about 68%. Nonetheless, the protein content of fermented prawn waste is comparable to the previous study by Attaya et al. (1998) and Fagbenro (1996), with several differences in process parameter. Attaya et al. (1998) reported that by using a ratio of 1 : 1.2 for prawn head and culture broth, the crude protein content in the fermented liquor was 44%. Whereas Fagbenro (1996) obtained 43% of crude protein after 30 days fermentation of African river prawn head with 5% (w/w) *L. plantarum* and 15% (w/w) cane molasses at 30 °C.

A study by Zakaria et al. (1998) demonstrated that horizontal bioreactor may be more suitable for large-scale application due to its easier separation process plus the cleaning process of the chitin sediment could be done in-situ. The horizontal position also had been identified as the ideal position to reduce the risk of product spoilage, and it provides ease of intermittent mixing by the motor-controlled rotation of the inner basket.

CONCLUSION

Protein liquor produced through the fermentation of prawn waste by LAB contained high protein (47%), moisture (92%) but low fiber (0.8%) contents; hence, it is suitable to be used as a partial substitute to the expensive imported fishmeal protein in the diet of aquaculture fish. However, two main problems when dealing with liquid product are storage and transportation. An added advantage of this process is the valuable by-product, i.e., chitin, which has many commercial applications such as in the cosmetic and wastewater treatment industries.

ACKNOWLEDGMENT

The authors would like to acknowledge the Ministry of Science, Technology and Innovation (MOSTI), Malaysia for funding the project via the E-ScienceFund.

REFERENCES

AOAC. (1980). Official Methods of Analytical Analysis (13th edition). (Ed. W. Horwitz), Association of Official Analytical Chemists, Washington D.C., 125.

Attaya Kungsuwan, Porathip Kiatkungwalkrai, Shrinavas Mukkas, Suwakee Chandr Krachang and William, Stevens. F. (1996). Protein and chitin from shrimp biowaste by fermentation using Lactobacilli. In: R.A.A Muzarelli (Ed.), *Chitin Enzymology*. Italy: Atec Edizioni. 573-580.

Axelsson, L. T. (1993). Lactic acid bacteria: classification and physiology. In Salminen, S. and Wright, S.V., (Eds). *Lactic Acid Bacteria* (p. 1-65). New York: Marcel Dekker Inc.

Brzeski, M. M. (1987). Chitin and chitosan-putting waste to good use. *INFOFISH Int.*. 5, 31-33.

Chaplin, M.F. and Kennedy, J.F. (1986). *Carbohydrate analysis a practical approach*. Washington D.C.: IRL Press. 2-3.

Fagbenro, O. A. (1996). Preparation, properties and preservation of lactic acid fermented shrimp heads. *Food Research International*. 29(7), 595-599.

Fanimo, A.O., Odugawa, O.O., Onitade, A.O., Olutunde, T.O. (2000). Protein quality of shrimp waste meal. *Journal of Bioresource Technology,* 72: 185-188.

Food and Agriculture Organization (2007). *The State of World Fisheries and Aquaculture 2006*. Rome: Food And Agriculture Organization.

Hall, G. M., Silva, S. D.,(1992). Lactic acid fermentation of scampi (*Penaeus monodon*) waste for chitin recovery. In Brine, C.J., Sandford, P.A., Zikakis, J.P. (Eds) *Advances in Chitin and chitosan*. (pp 633-668). London: Elsevier Applied Science.

Hamizatul Zakiah binti Daud (2000). *Pemencilan Bakteria Asid Laktik daripada Fermentasi Sisa Udang*. BSc. Thesis. Universiti Teknologi Malaysia, Malaysia.

Hassan, T. E, Health, J. L. (1986). Biological fermentation of fish waste for potential use in animal and poultry feeds. *Agricultural Wastes.* 15, 1-15.

Jay, J. M. (1992). *Modern Food Microbiology*. (4th edition). New York: Van Nostrand Reinhold.

Legaretta, G. I., Zakaria, Z., Hall, G. M. (1996). Lactic acid fermentation of prawn waste: comparison of commercial and isolated starter culture. In Domard A, Jeuniaux C, Muzarelli R. A. A., Roberts G. A. F. (Eds). *Advances in Chitin Science*. (p 396-406). France: Jacques Andre, Lyon.

Madigan, M. T., Martinko, J. M., Paker, J. Brock. (1997). *Biology of Microorganism*. (Eight editions). Englewood Cliffs: Prentice Hall.

Malaysian Fisheries Department (2004). *Annual Fisheries Statistic 2004*. Malaysian Fisheries Department, Malaysia.

Meyers, S. P. (1986). Utilization of shrimp processing wastes. *INFOFISH Marketing Dig*. 4(86), 18-19.

Nwanna, L. C. (2003). Nutritional Value and Digestibility of Fermented Shrimp Head Waste Meal by African Catfish, *Clarias gariepinus*. *Pakistan Journal of Nutrition*. 2(6), 339-345.

Ornum, J. V. (1992). Shrimp waste-must it be wasted. *INFOFISH Int*. 6, 48-52.

Raa, J. (1980). Biochemistry of microbial fish spoilage and preservation by lactic acid bacteria and added acid. In: S.O. Emejuaiwe, O. Ogunbi and S.O. Sanmi (Eds). *Global Impacts in Applied Microbiology*. London: Academis Press. p 8-16.

Rao, M. S., Munoz, J., Stevens, W. F. (2002). Critical factors in chitin production by fermentation of shrimp biowaste. *Applied Microbiol Biotechnology*. 54, 808-813.

Shahidi, F., and Synowiecki, J. (1991). Isolation and characterization of nutrients value-added products from snow crab (*Chinoecetes ipolio*) and Shrimp (*Pandalus borealis*) processing discards. *J. Agric. Food Chem*. 39, 1527-1532.

Shirai, K., Gurrero, I., Huetta, S., Saucedo, G., Castillo, A., Gonzalez, O., Hall, G.M. (2001). Effect of initial glucose concentration and inoculation level of lactic acid bacteria in shrimp waste ensilation. *Enzyme and Microbial* Technology. 28, 446-452.

Simpson, B. K. and Gagne, N. and Simpson, M. V. (1994). Bioprocessing of chitin and chitosan. In: A.M. Martin (Ed). *Fisheries Processing: Biotechnological Applications*. (p. 162-170). London: Chapman and Hall.

Soomroo, A. H., Masud, T., and Anwaar, K. (2002). Role of Lactic Acid Bacteria (LAB) in food preservation and Human Health-A review. *Pakistan Journal of Nutrition*. 1(1), 20-24.

Wyk, V. H. J. and Heydenrych, C. M. S. (1985). The production of naturally fermented fish silage using various lactobacilli and different carbohydrate sources. *Journal of Science Food Agricultural*. 36, 1093-1103.

Wood, B. (1998). *Microbiology of Fermented Foods*. (Vol. 1). New York: Blackie.

Zakaria. Z., Sharma, G., Hall, G. M. (1998). Lactic acid fermentation of scampi waste in a rotating bioreactor for chitin recovery. *Process Biochem*. 33, 1-6.

In: Bacteria in Environmental Biotechnology   ISBN 978-1-61728-350-5
Editor: W.A. Ahmad et al.   © 2011 Nova Science Publishers, Inc.

Chapter 6

THE REMOVAL OF HEXAVALENT CHROMIUM AND PHENOL USING LOCALLY ISOLATED BACTERIA

Mohd Saufi Mohd Sidek, Wan Azlina Ahmad and Shafinaz Shahir

ABSTRACT

Acinetobacter haemolyticus (*A. haemolyticus*), a locally isolated Cr(VI)-resistant-reducing bacterium, was evaluated for its ability to reduce phenol from simulated effluent and industrial wastewater. In suspended cells system, longer time was needed by the bacterium to completely reduce 90 mg L^{-1} Cr(VI) compared to the lower concentrations, indicating the influence of Cr(VI) toxicity on the survival of bacteria. The bacterium showed the ability to grow in up to 500 mg L^{-1} of phenol. However, this does not translate into high phenol degradation as relationship between *A. haemolyticus* and phenol was more via the adsorption process rather than degradation. In the immobilized cells system, a shorter time was required to achieve complete Cr(VI) reduction. The bacterium also showed substantial ability to reduce phenol. These conditions resulted from the favorable role of the support material in protecting the bacterium from toxicity effects (from Cr(VI) and phenol) and also retaining high number of bacterial cells.

INTRODUCTION

Water pollution may originate from many sources. Industrial activities are one of the examples, with strings of contaminants that include heavy metals, organics, oil and solids. An example for heavy metals contamination is hexavalent chromium Cr(VI), which is mainly used in industries such as leather tanning, metal finishing, petroleum refining, iron and steel (Laxman and More, 2002). Cr(VI) is one of the most dangerous pollutants, which is mainly due to its mutagenic and carcinogenicity, and is listed by USEPA as one the greatest threats to humans (Cheung and Hu, 2007). Chemical and physicochemical methods such as precipitation, adsorption and ionic exchange are the common practices used to remove the presence of chromium from wastewater. However, these methods are not cost effective, chemical and energy intensive, and also generate secondary pollution (Zhu et. al., 2006). In view of this, the use of biological approach is receiving more attention nowadays. The reduction of Cr(VI) using microorganism is more environmental friendly, with equal or better efficiency. Many bacterial species such as *Bacillus, Pseudomonas* and *Providencia* have been reported by other researchers to have the ability to reduce Cr(VI) into its less toxic state, Cr(III) form (Liu et. al., 2006 and Thacker et. al., 2006).

Organic contamination is frequently observed in the water system and can originate from different sources such as the household (detergent, washing liquid), cosmetic industry, petroleum industry, agriculture, mining industry and others (Zawala et. al., 2007). Some of these organic compounds such as benzene, toluene and phenol are toxic while others such as the residues of polycyclic aromatic hydrocarbon (PAH) may exert the mutagenic and carcinogenic effects (Chen et. al., 2005). Phenol and its related compounds are dangerous if inhaled, contacted or ingested, even at low concentrations. This makes it imperative to properly treat the phenol-contaminated wastewater before being discharged into the environment. Conventional treatment methods such as filtration, flotation and ion exchange are effective but are costly and energy intensive. Biological methods such as biodegradation and biosorption are gaining attention, as they are more effective and offer complete mineralization of the compound (Wei et. al., 2006). There are many studies that have been established about the microorganisms that can degrade phenol such as *Pseudomonads sp., Rodococcus sp., Brevibacillus sp.* and *Coprinus sp.* (Margesin et. al., 2004; Yang and Lee, 2001).

BACTERIA AND WASTEWATER

The bacterial strain used in this chapter was *A. haemolyticus*, isolated from a local batek (textile-related) manufacturing premise located in Kota Bharu, Kelantan, Malaysia (Zakaria et. al., 2006). It was identified using the 16S rRNA technique and deposited in Gene Bank with an accession number of EF 369508. It was grown in the presence of Cr(VI)-phenol and was monitored separately. Stock Cr(VI) and phenol solutions were prepared (1000 mg L^{-1}) and filter-sterilized before used. The bacterium (10% v/v) was monitored for growth in 30 and 60 mg L^{-1} of Cr(VI) and 50 and 100 mg L^{-1} of phenol, respectively. Medium containing Cr(VI) and phenol in the absence of bacteria acted as control.

Wastewater for the treatment purposes was collected at different sampling locations. For hexavalent chromium, the wastewater is collected from one local plating factory located in Pasir Gudang, Johor Bahru. For the phenol wastewater, effluent water from one refinery was selected. The wastewater collected was analyzed for its metal contents using the Inductively Coupled Plasma Mass Spectroscopy, ICP – MS at the Chemical Engineering Pilot Plant (CEPP), UTM. The phenol content in the wastewater was determined using the 4-aminoantipyrine method (Martin, 1947).

Profiles for the growth of *A. haemolyticus* in NB only, NB with Cr(VI) and NB with phenol at different phenol and Cr(VI) concentrations are shown in Figure 6.1.

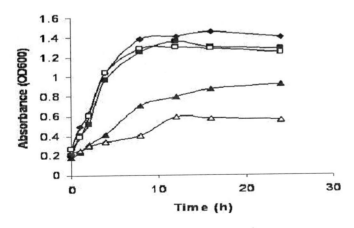

Figure 6.1. Growth profiles of *A. haemolyticus* in 30 mg L^{-1} Cr(VI) – (▲), 60 mg L^{-1} Cr(VI) – (Δ), 50 mg L^{-1} phenol – (■), 100 mg L^{-1} phenol – (□), in NB only – (◆).

Maximum growth of *A. haemolyticus* was obtained in the NB only with an OD_{600} of 1.44. However, the bacterial growth was slightly impeded when 50 and 100 mg L^{-1} of phenol were added into the growth medium. This may be due to the ability of the cells to utilize phenol as the carbon and energy source (Margesin et. al., 2004). The bacterial growth was severely affected in the presence of 30 and 60 mg L^{-1} of Cr(VI) with maximum OD_{600} values of 0.92 and 0.54, respectively. This justifiably signifies the effect of Cr(VI) toxicity towards bacterial survival in the growth medium (Zakaria et al., 2006). Cr(VI) is mutagenic to some bacterial cells as it has the ability to undergo one, two or three electron transfers, in order to reach its Cr(III) state. During this chain-like electron transfer reaction, the highly oxidizing reactive oxygen species (ROS) will be generated, which will directly interrupt with cell functions. Many bacteria have been reported to be able to utilize phenol as its carbon and energy sources up to initial phenol concentrations from 0 to 1000 mg L^{-1} (Jiang et. al., 2007). Profiles for heavy metals concentration in the Cr(VI) and phenol-containing wastewaters are as shown in Table 6.1. A relatively high Cr(VI), 58.91 mg L^{-1}, was determined in the wastewater, while phenol was only slightly higher than the stipulated discharge limit, i.e., 1.3 to 2.1 mg L^{-1} (Standard B, 1.0 mg L^{-1}; Department of Environment Malaysia, 2009). Other characteristics of the phenol-containing oil refinery wastewater are as follows: colour - greenish; pH, 9.5 to 9.9; temperature, 32.4 to 32.9 °C; dissolve oxygen, 12.95 to 13.45 mg L^{-1}; phenol, 1.3 to 2.1 mg L^{-1} (Standard B – 1.0 mg L^{-1}).

Table 6.1. Metal concentrations in raw Cr(VI)-containing wastewater (obtained from one electroplating premise in Pasir Gudang, Johor) and phenol-containing oil refinery wastewater (Port Dickson, Negeri Sembilan)

Element	Electroplating wastewater	Oil-refinery Wastewater	*Standard B (mg L^{-1})
Cr(VI)	58.91 + 9.32	0.21 + 0.03	0.05
Cd	0.01 + 0.01	0.01 + 0.01	0.02
Ni	0.14 + 0.01	0.35 + 0.13	1.00
Fe	3.70 + 0.03	25.88 + 14.36	5.00
As	0.08 + 0.01	0.04 + 0.01	0.10
Zn	0.13 + 0.02	4.99 + 4.87	2.00
Cu	0.06 + 0.01	0.34 + 0.22	1.00
Pb	0.01 + 0.01	0.08 + 0.04	0.50

* Standard B – permissible discharge limit for industrial wastewater outside the catchment area in Malaysia.

CR(VI) REDUCTION AND PHENOL DEGRADATION - BATCH SYSTEM (PLS CHANGE R IN CR TO SMALL R)

For the Cr(VI) reduction studies, 10% (v/v) inoculum was incubated in a series of 1 L Erlenmeyer flasks containing 100 mL of NB mixed with 10, 30, 60 and 90 mg L^{-1} of Cr(VI). The mixtures were then incubated at 30 $^{\circ}$C, 200 rpm for three to four days. Similar experimental setup minus the bacteria acted as the control. At various time intervals, Cr(VI) was determined using the DPC method. In the phenol degradation work, 10% (v/v) of inoculum was transferred into a series of 1 L Erlenmeyer flasks containing 10, 50, 100 and 500 mg L^{-1} of phenol prior to shaking at 200 rpm, 30 $^{\circ}$C for two to five days. Medium-containing phenol solutions without bacteria acted as the control. Periodical determination of phenol was carried out using the 4-aminoantipyrine method. Similar experimental setup was prepared for studies using both the Cr(VI) and phenol-containing industrial wastewaters. *A. haemolyticus* showed the ability to reduce 99% of 10 mg L^{-1} Cr(VI), 96% - 30 mg L^{-1}, 93% - 60 mg L^{-1} and 85% - 90 mg L^{-1} (Figure 6.2).

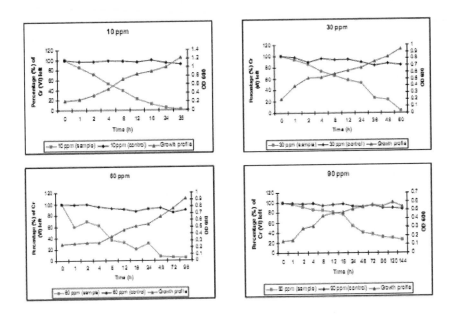

Figure 6.2. The relationship between Cr(VI) reduction and survival of *A. haemolyticus* in 10, 30, 60 and 90 mg Cr(VI) L^{-1}.

However, these Cr(VI) reduction abilities decrease with increasing Cr(VI) concentrations. This can be directly attributed to the toxic effects of Cr(VI) towards the bacterial cells (Yun – Guo et. al., 2008), as shown from the decreasing cells' survival (represented by OD600) when Cr(VI) was increased. *A. haemolyticus* showed the highest growth at 10 mg L^{-1} of Cr(VI) with OD$_{600}$ of 1.22. Upon increasing the Cr(VI) concentrations to 30 mg L^{-1}, the OD$_{600}$ was reduced to 0.94, followed by 0.90 at 60 mg L^{-1} and 0.52 at 90 mg L^{-1}. The lower cell concentrations present resulted in a prolonged time required to complete the Cr(VI) reduction process. As observed in this work, 144 h were needed by *A. haemolyticus* to reduce 85% of 90 mg L^{-1} of Cr(VI), while only 36 h were needed to reduce 99% of 10 mg L^{-1} Cr(VI). Similar observations have been reported by other researchers where a longer contact time was needed to completely reduce Cr(VI) at high initial Cr(VI) concentrations (Philip et. al., 1998; Shen and Wang, 1994). The important process in the reduction of Cr(VI) is the biotransformation of Cr(VI) to Cr(III) (Cheung and Hu, 2007). The mechanism of Cr(VI) reduction is species dependant and varies amongst the species. The anaerobic bacteria would use Cr(VI) as the terminal electron acceptor in their respiratory chain, while soluble enzymes are the main factor in the reduction process for the aerobic bacteria (Liu et. al., 2006). For Cr(VI) reduction from wastewater obtained from the electroplating premise, a total of 91% of the initial Cr(VI) of 58.91 mg L^{-1} was reduced after three days of contact time, which indicates the feasibility of employing this bacterium for industrial application. *A. haemolyticus* showed good growth in the presence of 10 to 500 mg L^{-1} of phenol with maximum OD$_{600}$ values of 1.36 (10 mg L^{-1}) and 0.94 (500 mg L^{-1}). However, this was not translated into high phenol degrading ability by the cells, as only 70.3% of phenol was degraded at initial phenol concentration of 10 mg L^{-1}, 60.8% for 50 mg L^{-1}, 28.8% for 100 mg L^{-1} and only 18.63% for 500 mg L^{-1} (Figure 6.3).

One plausible explanation for this condition is that phenol reduction may not be due to the degradation process only (Jiang et. al., 2007), instead co-occurring with the adsorption of phenol onto the cell's surface. Microbially mediated phenol degradation leads to the formation of carbon dioxide and water, with several intermediates such as benzoate, catechol, cis, cis-muconate, β-ketodipate, succinate and acetate (Tuah, 2006). Although many microorganisms can utilize and degrade phenol as their carbon and energy source, the mechanism of phenol degradation in *A. haemolyticus* has not been elucidated. *A. haemolyticus* also showed the ability to degrade 80.9% of the 1.3 to 2.1 mg L^{-1} phenol presence in the oil refinery effluent water after three days of contact time.

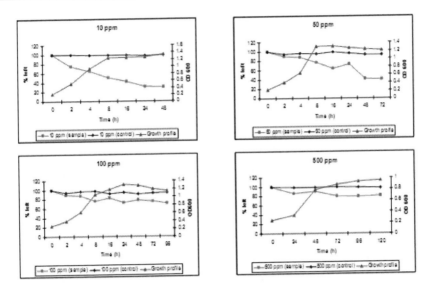

Figure 6.3. The relationship between phenol degradation and cells survival in 10, 50, 100 and 500 mg phenol L^{-1}.

CR(VI) REDUCTION AND PHENOL DEGRADATION-FLOW–THROUGH COLUMN SYSTEM (PLEASE CHANGE R IN CR TO SMALL R)

The bioreactor was set up using a glass column with the following specifications: inner diameter (I.D.) - 5.0 cm, outer diameter (O.D.) – 5.7 cm and height – 50 cm. Inlet and outlet points were set 5 and 2 cm from the top and bottom of the column. Both the inlet and outlet points were fitted with Teflon tubing; I.D. – 2.0 mm and O.D. – 4.0 mm. Inert stones were filled up to 98.2 cm^3 at the bottom of the column, followed by the insertion of wood husk to a volume of 589.1 cm^3, where this volume is considered as the working volume for the bioreactor. Another layer of inert stones was packed at the top of the wood husk for 98.2 cm^3, and an empty space about 196.4 cm^3 was left at the top of the column. The wood husk used as the support materials for the immobilization of *A. haemolyticus* was obtained from a local sawmill factory. The column was first rinsed with deionized water using a peristaltic pump (Eyela MP – 1000) to wash and remove large particulate substances on the support materials to prevent clogging, besides allowing the surface of the materials to obtain charges, which are required for bacterial attachment (Zakaria et. al., 2007).

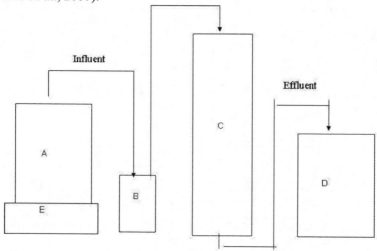

Figure 6.4. Schematic diagram for the Cr(VI) reduction/ phenol degradation system; A – influent/ holding tank, B – peristaltic pump, C – column/ bioreactor, D – effluent/ receiving tank, E – magnetic stirrer.

Following this, 1 L culture of a 12-h old *A. haemolyticus* was pumped continuously into the column at a flow rate of 2 mL min^{-1} for 24 h to ensure the initial formation of biofilm by the bacteria. The Cr(VI) reduction and phenol degradation system consists of the holding tank, outlet tank, peristaltic pump and the column or bioreactor (Figure 6.4).

Schott bottle, 1 L was used as the influent vessel (A), which contains a mixture of NB (nutrient) and wastewater (simulated or real waste). Final Cr(VI) or phenol concentrations in the mixture in (A) ranged from 10 to 150 mg L^{-1}. The pH of the effluent mixture was always maintained at 7.0 ± 0.2. The mixture was transferred into the bioreactor (C) using a peristaltic pump (B) where the Cr(VI) will be reduced to Cr(III) by the bacterial biofilm packed inside the bioreactor. The bioreactor effluent was then collected in the effluent tank (D) and determined for Cr(VI) (DPC method) and total Cr concentrations (AAS). Phenol was determined using the 4-aminoantipyrine method as follows (Martin, 1947): 0.3 mL of 2% (v/v) 4-aminoantipyrine and 1 mL of 2 N NH$_4$OH was added into 50 mL of sample, followed by thorough mixing. The mixture was then added with 1 mL of 2% (v/v) K$_3$(Fe(CN)$_6$), which will give rise to a red indophenol dye under alkaline condition. The absorbance was measured at OD_{460} (Genesys 20, Thermo Spectronic). The phenol concentration was calibrated against a phenol standard from $0.2 - 2.0$ mg L^{-1}.

Complete Cr(VI) reduction was achieved for 10, 30 and 60 mg L^{-1} Cr(VI) after 8 and 12 h of contact time, while a longer time, i.e., 20 h, was needed for 90 and 100 mg L^{-1}. However, only 90% of 150 mg L^{-1} of Cr(VI) were reduced after 20 h (Figure 6.5).

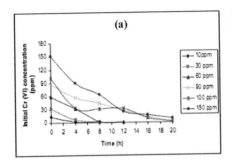 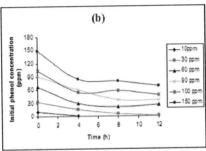

Figure 6.5. Cr(VI) reduction (a) and phenol degradation (b) by immobilized cells of *A. haemolyticus* at 10 to 150 mg L^{-1}.

The column-immobilized cells system showed a higher Cr(VI) reduction capacity (percentage of Cr(VI) reduced and contact time) compared to the batch system. Similar findings were also reported by Ying et. al. (2006) and Konovalova et. al. (2003). The presence of the support materials provides a protective shelter for the cells against the toxicity (Ying et. al., 2006) of either Cr(VI) or phenol, hence a higher number of cells survive compared to the free cells system where the extent of cells survival was directly governed by toxicity, especially for Cr(VI). According to the report by Chung et. al (2003), the immobilization of cells could alter the physiological features in metabolism such as the enhanced enzyme induction. Kim et. al (2001) reported that the immobilization of microorganisms into a packed column has certain advantages, such as high-cell concentration due to the formation of biofilm and active microorganism are held in stationary phase, which contributes to the better performance in the removal of toxic compound. The flow-through column system also showed good capability to reduce Cr(VI) in the electroplating wastewater where 99.1% of the 58.91 mg L^{-1} Cr(VI) were reduced after 6 h of contact time. This signifies the substantial role by the bacterial biofilm to reduce Cr(VI), as the abiotic control setup (i.e., minus the bacteria) were only responsible for 10% of the Cr(VI) reduction.

Complete phenol degradation was achieved for 10 and 30 mg L^{-1} phenol after a contact time of 4 and 12 h, respectively. Decreased phenol degradation was observed with increasing phenol concentrations with values of 54% for 60 mg L^{-1}, 47% - 90 mg L^{-1}, 56% - 100 mg L^{-1} and 53% - 150 mg L^{-1} (all after a contact time of 12 h). At certain levels of phenol concentration, microbial growth can be inhibited due to the effect of phenol on cell lysis (Monteiro et. al., 2000). The efficiency of an immobilized bacterial system to remove phenol (via degradation) shows its potential industrial application as opposed to the use of suspended cultures. Similar observation was also reported by Aksu and Bulbul (1999) and Chen et al. (2002). Immobilization protects the bacteria from the harmful effects of phenol toxicity besides maintaining cell growth and survival during the phenol degradation process (Chung et. al., 2003). For the phenol-containing oil refinery wastewater, almost complete phenol degradation (98.8%) was obtained after a contact time of 6 h.

CONCLUSION

A. haemolyticus showed the ability to cease Cr(VI) and phenol toxicity via the reduction and degradation processes. The bacterium showed good potential for industrial application, both via the suspended and immobilized cells system. The immobilized cells system displayed a much higher efficiency in terms of time needed and percentage of Cr(VI) reduced.

ACKNOWLEDGMENT

The authors would like to acknowledge the Ministry of Science, Technology and Innovation for the National Science Fellowship to Mohd Saufi Mohd Sidek.

REFERENCES

Aksu, Z., and Bulbul, G. 1999. Determination of the effective diffusion coefficient of phenol in Ca-alginated – immobilized *P. putida* beads. *Enzyme and Microbial Technology*. 25. 344 – 348.

Chen, K.C., Lin, Y.H., Chen, W.H., and Liu, Y.C. 2002. Degradation of phenol by PAA – immobilized *Candida tropicalis*. *Enzyme and Microbial Technology*. 31. 490 – 497.

Chen, Y., Wang, C. and Wang, Z. 2005. Residues and source identification of persistent organic pollutants in farmland soil irrigated by effluents from biological treatment plants. *Environment International*. 31. 778 – 783.

Cheung K. H and Hu, J.D. 2007. Mechanism of hexavalent chromium detoxification by microorganisms and bioremediation application potential: A review. *International Biodeterioration and Biodegradation*. 59. 8 – 15.

Chung, T. P., Tseng, H.Y., and Juang, R.S. 2003. Mass transfer effect and intermediate detection for phenol degradation in immobilized *Pseudomonas putida* systems. *Process Biochemistry*. 38. 1497 – 1507.

Department of Environment, Environmental Quality Report 2003, Ministry of Science Technology and Innovation Malaysia, 2004.

Greenberg, A.E., Trussell, R.R., and Clesceri, L.S. 1985. Standard Methods for the Examination of Water and Wastewater, 16th ed., APHA, New York.

Jiang, Y., Wen, J., Bai, J., Jia, X., and Hua, Z. 2007. Biodegradation of phenol at high initial concentration by *Alcaligenes faecalis*. *Journal of Hazardous Materials*. doi:10.1016/j.jhazmat.2007.05.031.

Kim, J.H., Oh, K.Y., Lee, S.T., Kim, S.W., and Hong, S.I. 2001. Biodegradation of phenol and chlorophenols with defined mixed culture in shake flasks and a packed bed reactor. *Process Biochemistry*. 37. 1367 – 1373.

Konovalova, V.V., Dmytrenko, G.M., Nigmatullin, R.R., Bryk, M.T., and Gvozdyak, P.I. 2003. Chromium (VI) reduction in a membrane bioreactor with immobilized *Pseudomonas* cells. *Enzyme and Microbial Technology*. 33. 899 – 907.

Laxman R.S. and More S. 2002. Reduction of hexavalent chromium by *Streptomyces griseus, Minerals Engineering*. 15. 831 – 837.

Liu, Y.G., Xu, W.H., Zeng, G.M., Li, X., and Gao, H. 2006. Cr(VI)reduction by *Bacillus sp.* isolated from chromium landfill. *Process Biochemistry*. 41. 1981 – 1986.

Margesin R., Fonteyne P.A. and Redl B. 2004. Low temperatures biodegradation of high amounts of phenol by *Rhodococcus spp.* and *basidiomycetus* yeasts. *Research in Microbiology*. 156. 68 – 75.

Martin, R.W. 1949. Rapid colorimetric estimation of phenol. *Anal. Chem.* 21. 1419 – 1420.

Monteiro, A.M.G., Boaventura, A.R., and Rodrigues, A.E. 2000. Phenol biodegradation by *Pseudomonas putida* DSM 548 in a batch reactor. *Biochemistry Engineering Journal*. 6. 45 – 49.

Philip, L., Iyengar, L., and Venkobachar, C. 1998. Cr(VI)reduction by *Bacillus coagulans* isolated from contaminated soils. *J. of Environ. Eng.* 124 (12). 1165 – 1170.

Shen, H. and Wang, Y.T. 1994. Biological reduction of chromium by *E.coli. J. of Environ. Eng.* 120. 560 – 572.

Thacker U., Parikh R. and Shouche Y. 2006. Hexavalent chromium reduction by *Providencia sp. Process Biochemistry*. 41. 1332 – 1337.

Tuah M. P. 2006. The performance of phenol biodegradation by *Candida tropicalis RETC Cr1* using batch and fed-batch fermentation techniques. Universiti Teknologi Malaysia. PhD Thesis.

Wei, G., Yu, J., Zhu, Y., Chen, W., and Wang, L. 2006. Characterization of phenol degradation by *Rhizobium* sp. CCNWTB 701 isolated from *Astragalus chrysopteru* in mining tailing region, *Journal of Hazardous Material*. doi:10.1016/j.jhazmat.05.058.

Yang, C.F., and Lee, C.M. 2001. Enrichment, isolation and characterization of phenol degrading *Pseudomonas resinovorans* strain P-1 and *Brevibacillus sp*. strain P-6. *International Biodeterioration and Biodegradation*. 59. 206 -210.

Ying, W., Ye, T., Bin, H., Hua – Bing, Z., Jian – nan, B., and Bao – li, C. 2006. Biodegradation of phenol by free and immobilized *Acinetobacter sp*. strain PD12. *J. of Environ. Science*. 19. 222 – 225.

Yun-Guo, L., Cui, P., Wen-Bin, X., Guang-Ming, Z., Ming, Z., Yuan-Yuan, L., Jie, K. and Chao, H. 2008. Simultaneous removal of Cr(VI)and phenol in consortium culture of *Bacillus sp*. and *Pseudomonas putida Migula* (CCTCC AB92019). *Transactions of Nonferrous Metals Society of China*. Vol 18. 1014 – 1020.

Zakaria, Z.A. 2006. Development of bacterial based remediation system for the removal of Chromium (VI) from electroplating industrial effluent. Universiti Teknologi Malaysia. PhD Thesis.

Zakaria, Z. A., Zakaria, Z., Surif, S. and Ahmad, W.A. 2007. Hexavalent chromium reduction by *Acinetobacter haemolyticus* isolated from heavy metal contaminated wastewater. *Journal of Hazardous Material*. 146: 30 - 38.

Zawala J., Swiech K. and Malysa K. 2007. A simple physicochemical method for detection of organic contaminations in water. *Colloids and Surfaces A:Physicochemical and Engineering Aspects.* 302. 293 – 300.

Zhu, W., Chai, L., Ma, Z., Wang, Y., Xiao, H., and Zhao, K. 2006. Anaerobic reduction of hexavalent chromium by bacterial cells of i strain Ch1. *Microbial Research,.*doi:10.1016/2006.09.008.

In: Bacteria in Environmental Biotechnology   ISBN 978-1-61728-350-5
Editor: W. A. Ahmad et al.   © 2011 Nova Science Publishers, Inc.

Chapter 7

THE KINETICS OF PHENOL DEGRADATION BY FREE AND IMMOBILIZED CELLS OF *PSEUDOMONAS SP.*

*Firdausi Razali, Mailin Mison
and Sabri Sethpa*

ABSTRACT

The kinetics of phenol degradation by an immobilized-bacterial system was carried out in a packed reactor operating in a repeated batch culture. The phenol-degraders used, i.e., *Pseudomonas sp.*, were locally isolated from water sample obtained from one residential wastewater treatment plant and soil sample from the wastewater discharge area of one oil-processing industry. The reactor was packed with either bio-ceramic or sponge as support material with bio-ceramic showing a higher ability to trap 1.8 times more bacterial cells than sponge, which is advantageous for phenol degradation. A continuous 24-hour cycle using influent flow rate of 2.5 mL min^{-1}, revealed that the bio-ceramic grown cells were capable to completely mineralized 1000 mg L^{-1} of phenol in six changes of phenol solutions compared to 90% phenol degradation by the sponge-grown cells. Immobilized cells showed a phenol tolerance level of 2000 mg L^{-1} compared to 1000 mg L^{-1} for the suspended cells. Outcomes of this study offer useful guidelines in evaluating potential phenol degraders from the environment and in treating phenolic contaminants using packed reactor system.

INTRODUCTION

Phenolic compounds are well-known components in industrial wastewaters including the steel industries, pharmaceutical, petrochemical, oil refineries, textiles and coal refining (Nuhoglu and Yalcin, 2004). Traditionally, phenol removal is carried out by costly physicochemical methods, but recently biological treatment has received widespread attention due to its low-cost and the possibility of complete phenol complete mineralization (Collins and Daugulis, 1997). Biodegradation is referred to as the biological transformation of phenol to another form of non-toxic compounds (Grady, 1985). It involves cleavage of the benzene ring mediated by metabolically dependent intracellular enzymatic reaction (Kumar et al., 2004). Many aerobic bacteria are capable of using aromatic compounds as their sole carbon and energy source, such as *Pseudomonas sp.*, *Candida tropicalis*, *Azotobacter sp.*, *Rhodococcus sp.*, *Alcaligenes sp.* and *Acinetobacter sp.* (Prieto et al., 2002; Chen et al., 2002; Hughes and Bayly, 1983; Valenzuela et al., 1997; Hao et al., 2002). The use of pure cultures, especially adapted to metabolize the contaminant, can be envisaged as an attractive alternative (Nurdan and Azmi, 2005). Acclimatization of the microorganisms overcomes the substrate inhibition problems that normally occurred in phenol biodegradation at high concentration (Lob and Tar, 2000). Certain intracellular enzymes were induced during the acclimatization stage so that the microbes are able to take part in the reaction (Kumar et al., 2004). There has been an increasing interest towards the use of immobilized microorganisms to remove phenol from aqueous solutions, since this technology offer many advantages over suspended cultures (Chen et al., 2002; Prieto et al., 2002). Besides providing high cell concentration, the im-mobilized-cells system eliminates the need for cell recovery processes as well as being resistant to washout and phenol shock loading (Kim et al., 2001). Various materials have been used as matrix for immobilization of cells such as calcium alginate (Chung et al., 2003), chitin and cellulose derivatives (Arica et al., 1993), polyurethane foam (Nakamura et al., 1997), nylon sponge (Haapala and Linko, 1993), ceramic (Prieto et al., 2002) and silica-based particle (Nurdan and Azmi, 2005).

ACCLIMATIZATION OF BACTERIA IN PHENOL

The bacteria were isolated from a water sample obtained from one residential wastewater treatment plant and a soil sample from the wastewater discharge area of one oil-processing industry. The samples were added into Ramsay medium (Ramsay et al., 1983) containing 1 g L^{-1} glucose as sole carbon source before incubation for 24 h. The grown cultures were further spiked with 0.3 g L^{-1} phenol at room temperature for 24 h and shaken at 150 rpm (Infors AG, Switzerland). The treated samples (0.1 mL) were then serially diluted, and single bacterial colony was obtained on Nutrient Agar (NA). The single bacterial isolates were then characterized for Gram, catalase, oxidase, urease, citrate and indole properties using the Bergey's Manual of Determinative of Bacteriology (Goodfeelow, 1994). The Ramsay medium was supplemented with NH_4NO_3, 2.0 g L^{-1}; KH_2PO_4, 0.5 g L^{-1}; K_2HPO_4, 1.0 g L^{-1}; $MgSO_4.7H_2O$, 0.5 g L^{-1}; $CaCl_2.2H_2O$, 0.01 g L^{-1}; KCl, 0.1 g L^{-1} and yeast extract, 0.06 g L^{-1}. It was sterilized via autoclaving at 121 °C for 15 mins, while phenol (0.3 g L^{-1}) was separately sterilized using 0.45 μm membrane filtration. The bacterial isolates were acclimatized in phenol using the following procedures: a 24 h culture (10% v/v) grown in Ramsay medium supplemented with 1 g L^{-1} glucose was inoculated into a fresh Ramsay medium containing 0.8 g L^{-1} glucose and 0.2 g L^{-1} phenol, followed by agitation at 150 rpm for 24 h at room temperature. Similar procedures were repeated using decreasing concentrations of glucose and increasing concentrations of phenol.

During the culture enrichment stage in the Ramsay medium, eight isolates were originally isolated. Upon addition of phenol, only four isolates survived, hence identified as phenol degraders. The isolates were denoted as RWC - Sma, RWC - Crl, ISC - Ycr and ISC - Tra (RWC - Residential Wastewater Culture, ISC - Industrial Soil Culture). RWC - Crl was a Gram negative rod while RWC – Sma, ISC - Ycr and ISC - Tra were all Gram negative cocci (Table 7.1). All isolates also showed positive oxidase and catalase tests. Hence, the microbes can be classified as an aerobic microorganism. According to the Bergey's Manual of Determinative Bacteriology (MacFaddin, 2000), 85% of the results showed similar characteristics with *Pseudomonas sp.*, *Alcaligenes sp.* or *Azotobacter sp.* These results are consistent with previous reported studies (Hannaford and Kuek, 1999; Hughes and Bayly, 1983; Moustafa, 2003).

The decrease of glucose concentration was compensated by phenol to maintain total carbon at 1000 mg L^{-1}. The results of the specific phenol degradation rate for all isolates are summarized in Figure 7.1.

Table 7.1. Morphological and biochemical characterizations of isolates

Test	Isolates			
	RWC-Sma	RWC-Cr1	ISC-Tra	ISC-Ycr
Gram staining	-	-	-	-
Shape	rod	cocci	cocci	cocci
Catalase	+	+	+	+
Oxidase	+	+	+	+
Urease	-	-	-	-
Citrate	-	-	+	-
Indole	+/-	+/-	+/-	+

The specific degradation rate is defined based on the relationship between substrate consumption and the biomass growth within 1 h in the fermentation process (Santos and Linardi, 2003). As all three other isolates demonstrated specific degradation rate of below ~~than~~ 0.01 g phenol g^{-1} cell h^{-1} at all phenol concentrations, RWC - Cr1 continued to perform excellently even at 1000 mg L^{-1} phenol. The increase in degradation rate by RWC - Cr1 obviously obeyed the first order kinetic. Isolate RWC - Tr1 seemed to prefer phenol to glucose as carbon and energy source, hence suggesting its selection as the phenol degrader for subsequent works. During the acclimatization process, certain enzymes in bacteria were induced so that they are available to take part in the metabolism reaction (Kumar et al., 2004).

Acclimatization also provides sufficient time for small populations of mineralizing organisms to become sufficiently large to bring a detectable loss of the chemical (Bruce et al., 1997). Figure 7.2 summarizes the results of the specific phenol degradation rate of four isolates in various glucose to phenol ratios. Based on the profiles depicted in Figures 7.1 and 7.2, two early conclusions can be made. Firstly, while acclimatization did not result in marked increase in the specific phenol degradation rate for the RWC - Cr1 isolate, all three other isolates demonstrated encouraging improvement in terms of the difference (in percentage) between the specific phenol degradation rates for raw and acclimatized bacterial isolates (Figure 7.3).

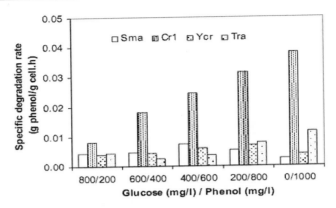

Figure 7.1. Specific phenol degradation rate by four raw isolates in various glucose to phenol ratios.

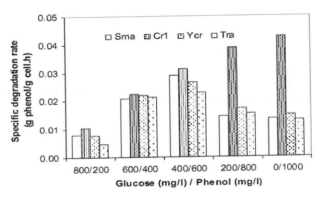

Figure 7.2. Specific phenol degradation rate by acclimatized cultures in various glucose to phenol ratios.

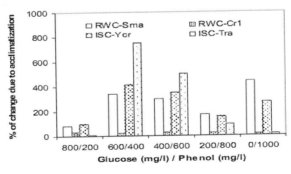

Figure 7.3. Change to the specific phenol degradation rates (in percentage) after the bacterial isolates was acclimatized to phenol.

Table 7.2. Phenol degradation studies using other types of bacteria

Bacterium	System	Phenol mg L^{-1}	Specific growth rate, μ (h^{-1})	Reference
P. putida	Batch	1200	NA	Hannaford and Kuek (1999)
P. putida	Batch	600	0.17	Chung et al. (2003)
P.putida	Continuous	1000	0.03	Gonzalez et al. (2001)
Acinetobacter sp.	Batch	500	NA	Kumaran and Paruchuri (1997)
Klebsiella sp.	Batch	230	NA	Okaygun et al. (1992)
P. putida	Batch	100	0.16	Monteiro et al. (2000)
*RWC-Cr1	Batch	1000	0.09	This study

Pseudomonas sp., Alcaligenes sp. or Azotobacter sp.

Secondly, the acclimatization process was successful in increasing the specific phenol degradation rate until 600 mg L^{-1} phenol. However, an inhibitory effect was observed beyond this level based on the gradual decrease in the specific degradation rate, a condition also reported by Monteiro et al. (2000). The ISC - Tra was also noted as isolate with the highest tolerant to phenol (based on the 750% change at 600 mg L^{-1} phenol), while acclimatization may not be necessary for the RWC - Cr1 isolate. The superiority of the RWC - Cr1 isolate to degrade 1000 mg L^{-1} phenol is comparable to that reported by other researchers (Table 7.2). It is important to note that 1000 mg L^{-1} phenol tested on RWC - Cr1 may not be the maximum tolerable level, since we have not yet tested it beyond this concentration.

PHENOL DEGRADATION BY SUSPENDED AND IMMOBILIZED CELLS

Active cells (10% v/v) were inoculated into 100 mL Ramsay medium added with 200 to 2500 mg L^{-1} phenol in a series of 250 mL Erlenmeyer flasks.

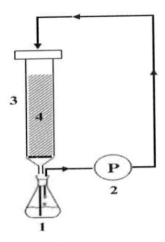

Figure 7.4. Degradation of phenol using the immobilized cells system; 1) feed reservoir 2) peristaltic pump 3) packed column and 4) support.

The mixtures were then agitated at room temperature and monitored for phenol concentration until complete phenol degradation was obtained. For the immobilized cells system, a 7-cm (i.d) and 40-cm (length) column was packed with either 500 g of bio-ceramic (mixture between hwang-to and oyster shells from Korea) or 5 g of sponge, as support materials. These materials were chosen as carriers due to their inert and highly porous nature. A distilled water suspended bacterial biomass was then continuously circulated into the column to immobilize the cells onto the column support material. The phenol degradation was then performed batch-wise by passing different changes of 600 mL of 1000 mg L^{-1} phenol at 2.5 mL min^{-1} through the column. This gave a total of six passes in 24 h. The experimental set up is illustrated in Figure 7.4.

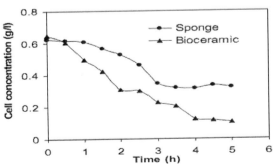

Figure 7.5. Profiles of cell concentrations in distilled water during immobilization onto sponge and bio-ceramic as carrier material.

The biomass concentration was estimated at OD_{600} (Hannaford and Kuek, 1999). Phenol concentration in sample was assayed using the colorimetric method as follows (Box, 1981): the culture supernatant was obtained via centrifugation at 10000 rpm for 10 mins. The supernatant (2 mL) was then added with 0.3 mL of sodium carbonate (200 g L^{-1}) and 0.1 mL of the Folin-Ciocalteau reagent followed by a 60 min incubation at room temperature. The mixture was then determined for phenol at OD_{750} using spectrophotometer. The instrument was calibrated against 0 - 0.01 g L^{-1} of phenol.

The support material or carrier in immobilization system may affect the phenol degradation performance. The immobilization of cells onto the carrier materials shows that the cell concentration in distilled water gradually declined until it reached the equilibrium state after 4 h of contact time (Figure 7.5). The reduction of cell concentrations indicates adsorption onto the surface of the carrier (Nurdan and Azmi, 2005). The results revealed that bio-ceramic had better cell adsorptive ability, i.e., 0.543 g cell L^{-1} as compared to 0.301 g cell L^{-1} in sponge (Figure 7.5).

The immobilized-cells were able to carry out complete degradation of 1000 mg L^{-1} phenol after a contact time of 24 h. For the control reactor, i.e., column packed with support material only (bio-ceramic) without the presence of bacterial cells, around 823 mg L^{-1} of phenol remained in the solution (Figure 7.6).

The decrease in phenol concentration for the control column can be attributed to the adsorption of phenol onto the support's surface (Nurdan and Azmi, 2005) with a maximum specific adsorption capacity of 0.354 mg L^{-1} phenol gram^{-1} bio-ceramic.

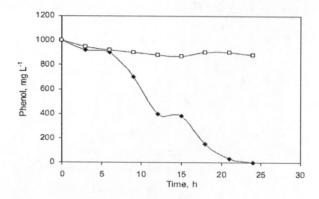

Figure 7.6. Degradation of 1000 mg L^{-1} phenol with (♦) and without (□) the presence of immobilized - culture.

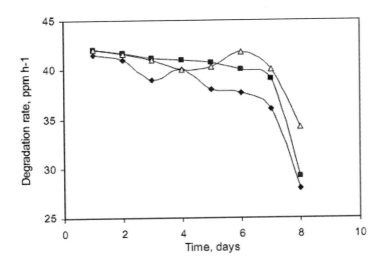

Figure 7.7. The effect of the support's diameter on the phenol degradation rate by immobilized – culture; (△) - 0.5 cm, (■) – 1.0 cm, (♦) – 1.5 cm.

Taking into consideration this low adsorption capacity by the support material, i.e., bio-ceramic, phenol degradation for the test reactor were assumed to be solely contributed by the microbial degradation. Larger particles increased their distances and significantly enhanced the problem of lower mass and gas transfer (Chung et al., 2003). In addition, the distances among supports reduced the surface area-to-volume ratio that resulted in poorer degradation rates due to relatively smaller cell populations per particle. The ability of bio-ceramic to trap and retain high amount of bacteria is important, as this is directly related to the extent of phenol degradation. The influence of the bio-ceramic's diameter on the phenol degradation rate (ppm h[-1]) is shown in Figure 7.7.

The use of bio-ceramic (support) with a diameter of greater than 1.0 cm resulted in decline degradation rate. Nevertheless, all the different support diameters used experienced similar sharp decline of phenol degradation rate after seven days of operation. However, it is recommended to use 1.0 cm of particle or less to give consistent phenol removal performance. It is also important to note that the packed reactor runs with different sets of operating conditions (e.g., loading rate, column diameter, etc.) would result in different observations. For example, increasing the loading rate would result in the detachment of bacterial cells from the support material, leading to the decline in the phenol degradation rate (Figure 7.8).

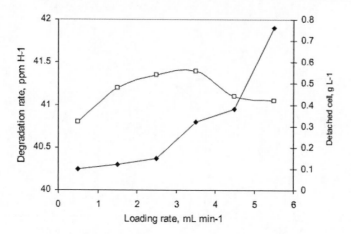

Figure 7.8. The effect of loading rate on phenol degradation rate (□) and cell detachment (♦).

Increased phenol degradation rates were observed up to a phenol loading rate of 3.5 mL min^{-1}. However, the degradation rate began to decrease when the loading rates were increased to 4.5 and 5.5 mL min^{-1}. This coincides perfectly with the increase in cell detachment from the bioreactor (g cell L^{-1}). Meanwhile, the loading rate of 2.5 mL min^{-1} was determined as optimum to give both highest degradation rate and reasonable cell detachment. Optimum loading rate ensures that sufficient time is given for the transport of phenol to the immobilized cells. At high loading rate, phenol would have an insufficient time to diffuse within the carrier particles, resulting in lower substrate bioconversion rate (Nurdan and Azmi, 2005). From the process point of view, high throughput is favorable; however this may lead to cell washout and lack of solid-liquid equilibrium. Both would significantly reduce the phenol removal capacity. As depicted in Figure 7.9, maximum phenol degradation rate without nutrient supplement would only last for three days.

Insufficient nutrient in the medium caused more cells to be killed and detached from supports (Chen et al., 2002). The supplementation of nutrients, however, extended the degradation rate limit up to seven days. This can be attributed to the role of nutrients in maintaining high cell number and the attenuation of phenol toxicity (Lob and Tar, 2000). In this study, phenol was used as the carbon source while other nutrients (nitrogen, etc.) are limited. By comparing the result of phenol degradation rates by cultures with and without nutrient supplementation, the level of limitation could be easily estimated.

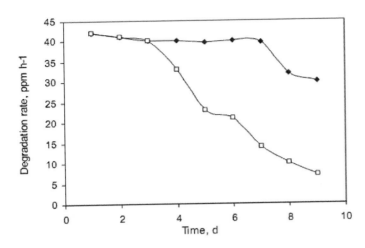

Figure 7.9. The effect of nutrient supplementation on phenol degradation rate (ppm h-1) by the immobilized cells; without nutrient (□) – without nutrient, (♦) – with nutrient.

The immobilized cultures were also able to completely degrade 1000 mg L^{-1} phenol in the repeated-batch mode (Figure 7.10). This complete phenol degradation was achieved until the seventh batch before experiencing the first decline in the eighth batch. That means the culture endured 42 cycles of total 4.2 L of 1000 mg L^{-1} phenol solution in seven days that corresponds to a specific phenol removal of 42 mg^{-1} h^{-1}.

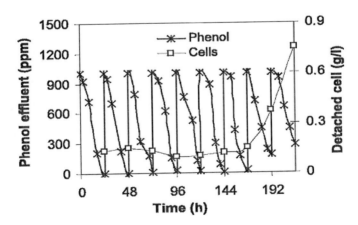

Figure 7.10. Phenol concentration in the effluent portion (ppm) in repeated-batch mode after nine days of bioreactor operation..

Similar to what was reported earlier, the decline in phenol degradation also coincides with cell detachment from the bioreactor, which was determined at OD_{600}. In a solid support, microbes form a biofilm, which is governed by the substrate diffusion limitations (Shuler and Kargi, 2002). Likewise, diffusional limitations may cause inadequate supply of substrate, oxygen, or nutrient to the inner portions of the biofilm, which may weaken the biofilm matrix and cause cell death. This circumstance was indicated by the increase of cell detachment. The immobilized cultures in this study showed excellent phenol degradation, even at 2000 mg L^{-1}. However, the phenol degradation activity for the suspended cells was completely inhibited beyond this concentration. A similar situation was reported by Loh et al. (2001). The higher phenol degradation capacity for the immobilized compared to the suspended cells may be due to the protective role of the support material against phenol toxicity (Chen et al., 2002) and because the cells were held on a stationary carrier surface (Kim et al., 2001). At 2000 mg L^{-1} phenol, the rate of phenol degradation declined significantly. However, it is estimated that the degradation activity would still occur beyond this concentration. It is worthy to note that immobilization has extended the volumetric degradation rate (mg phenol L^{-1} h^{-1}) limit of the microbe, especially at higher phenol concentrations (Figures 7.11 and 7.12).

Bio-ceramic-immobilized *Pseudomonas sp.* showed the ability to completely degrade 1000 mg L^{-1} phenol up to seven consecutive batches before experiencing the first decline in the eighth batch. A much lower performance was observed for the sponge-immobilized culture, where only 90% of the 1000 mg L^{-1} phenol was degraded when five batches of solution were fed continuously (Figure 7.13).

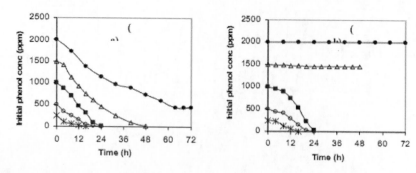

Figure 7.11. Removal of 250 to 2500 mg L^{-1} phenol by (a) immobilized and (b) suspended cells.

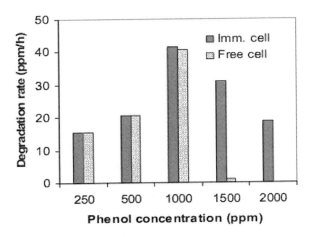

Figure 7.12. Phenol degradation rate by the immobilized and suspended cells.

The higher phenol degrading ability for the bio-ceramic-immobilized cells can be attributed to the higher cells' adsorptive ability as well as greater presence of micropores that provides high surface area for cells' attachment. This can be substantiated from a report by Xiangchun et al. (2003), where rapid formation of biofilm on the bio-ceramic carrier was observed. However, sponge may have an advantage in terms of industrial applicability, as it is much lighter than bio-ceramic, hence the easiness of handling and maintenance.

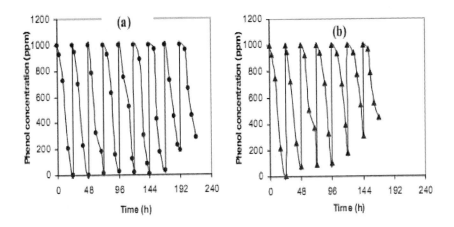

Figure 7.13. Profiles for phenol concentrations in solution during the degradation by (a) bio-ceramic and (b) sponge-immobilized cells of *Pseudomonas sp.*

CONCLUSION

This work has provided an initial insight into the potential application of bacteria as a tool to remove phenol contamination in the water system. The use of local isolates entrapped in the cheap and easy-to-handle support material, such as bio-ceramic and sponge, increased the attractiveness of this process.

ACKNOWLEDGMENTS

This work was supported by the Universiti Teknologi Malaysia (UTM) Short-Term Grant and the UTM-PTP Scholarship (to Mrs. Mailin). The authors are grateful to the technicians and students in the Department of Bioprocess Engineering, Faculty of Chemical Engineering and Natural Resources Engineering, UTM for their contributions and technical support in completing this study.

REFERENCES

Arica, M.Y., Sharif, F.A., Alaeddinoglu, N.G., Hasirci, N., Hasirci, V. (1993). Covalent entrapment of Aspergillus niger on pHEMA membrane: application to continuous-flow reactors. *Journal Chemical Technology Biotechnology.* 58, 281–285.

Bruce, A.W., Stephen, H.J. and Martin, A. (1987). Explanation for the acclimation period preceding the mineralization of organic chemical in aquatic environments. *Applied and Environmental Microbiology* 53:791-796.

Chen, K.C., Lin, Y.H., Chen, W.H. and Liu, Y.C. (2002). Degradation of phenol by PAA-immobilized *Candida tropicalis. Enzyme and Microbial Technology* 31:490-497.

Chung, T.P., Tseng, H.Y. and Juang, R.S. (2003). Mass transfer effect and intermediate detection for phenol degradation in immobilized *Pseudomonas putida* systems. *Process Biochemistry* 38: 1497-1507.

Collins, L.D. and Daugulis, A.J. (1997). Characterization and optimization of a two-phase partitioning bioreactor for the biodegradation of phenol. *Applied Microbial Biotechnology* 48: 18-22.

Gonzalez, G., Herrera, G., Garcia, M.T. and Pena, M. (2001). Biodegradation of phenolic industrial wastewater in a fluidized bed bioreactor with immobilized cells of *Pseudomonas putida*. *Bioresource Technology* 80: 137-142.

Goodfeelow M. (1994). Bergey's manual of determinative bacteriology 9th edition. Williams and Wilkins. London.

Grady, C.P. (1985). Biodegradation: its measurement and microbiological basis. *Biotechnology Bioengineering*. 27: 660-674.

Hao, O.J., Kim, M.H, Seager, E.A. and Kim, H. (2002). Kinetics of Phenol and Chlorophenol Utilization by Acinetobacter species. *Chemosphere* 46: 797-807.

Haapala, A., Linko, S. (1993). Production of Phanerochaete chrysosporium lignin peroxidase under various culture conditions. *Applied Microbiology Biotechnology*. 40, 494–498.

Hannaford, A.M. and Kuek, C. (1999). Aerobic batch degradation of phenol using immobilized *Pseudomonas putida*. *Journal of Industrial Microbiology and Biotechnology*. 22:121-126.

Hughes, E. J. and Bayly, R. C. (1983). Control of catechol meta cleavage pathway in *Ralstonia eutropha*. *Journal Bacteriology*. 154: 1363-1370.

Kim, J.H., Oh, K.K., Lee, S.T., Kim, S.W. and Hong, S.I. (2001). Biodegradation of phenol and chlorophenols with defined mixed culture in shake-flasks and a packed bed reactor. *Process Biochemistry*. 37.1367-1373.

Kumar, A., Kumar, S. and Kumar, S. (2004). Biodegradation kinetics of phenol and cathecol using *Pseudomonas putida* 1194. *Biochemical Engineering Journal*. 22: 151-159.

Kumaran, P. and Paruchuri, Y.L. (1997). Kinetics of phenol biotransformation. *Water Resource*. 31: 11-22.

Lob, K.C. and Tar, P.P. (2000). Effect of Additional Carbon Source on Biodegradation of Phenol. *Bulletin of Environmental Contamination and Toxicology*. 64: 756-767.

Loh, K.-C., Chung, T.-S., Ang, W.-F., 2000. Immobilized-cell membrane bioreactor for high-strength phenol wastewater. *Journal Environmental. Engineering*. 126, 75–79.

MacFaddin, J.F.(2000). Biochemical test for identification of medical bacteria. Williams and Wilkins. London.

Monteiro, A.M.G., Boaventura, A.R. and Rodrigues, A.E. (2000). Phenol biodegradation by *Pseudomonas putida* DSM 548 in a batch reactor. *Biochemical Engineering Journal* 6:45–49.

Moustafa, E.A. (2003). Biological degradation of substrates mixtures composed of phenol, benzoat, acetate by *Burkolderia cepacia G4*. Dissertation Ph.D. University of Carolo-Wilhelmina, Germany.

Nakamura, Y., Sawada, T., Sungusi, M.G., Kobayashi, F., Kuwahara, M., Ito, H. (1997). Lignin peroxidase production by *Phanerochaete chrysosporium. Journal of Chemical Engineering Japan.* 30, 1–6.

Nuhoglu, A. and Yalcin, B. (2004). Modeling of phenol removal in a batch reactor. *Process Biochemistry* 1-7.

Nurdan, K.P. and Azmi, T. 2005. Biodegradation of phenol by *Pseudomonas putida* immobilized on activated pumice particles. *Process Biochemistry.* 48: 1807-1814.

Okaygun, M.S., Green, L.A. andAkgerman, A.(1992). Effects of consecutive pulsing of an inhibitory substrate on biodegradation kinetics. *Environment Science Technology.* 26:1746-1752.

Prieto, M.B., Hidalgo, A., Serra, J.L. and Lama, M.J. 2002. Degradation of phenol by *Rhodococcus erythropolis* UPV-1 immobilized on Biolite in a packed-bed reactor. *Journal of Biotechnology.* 97: 1-11

Ramsay, B.A, Cooper, D.G. Margaritis, A. and Zajic, J.E. (1983). *Rhodochorous* Bacteria: Biosurfactant Production and Demulsifying Microbial Enhanced Oil Recovery 61-65.

Santos, V.L. and Linardi, V.R. (2003). Biodegradation of phenol by filamentous fungi isolated from industrial effluents-identification and degradation potential. *Process Biochemistry* 39:1001-1006.

Shuler, M.L. and Kargi, F. 2002. Bioprocess Engineering-Basic Concepts. 2nd Ed. Prentice Hall PTR, Turkey. 266 pp.

Valenzuela, J., Bumann, U., Cespedes, R., Padila, R. and Gonzalez, B. (1997). Degradation of chlorophenols by *Alcaligenes eutrophus* JMP134 (pJP4) in bleached kraft mill effluent. *Applied Environment Microbiology* 63:227–32.

Xiangchun, Q., Hanchang, S., Yongming, Z., Jianlong, W. and Yi, Qian. (2003). Biodegradation of 2,4-dichlorophenol in an air-lift honeycomb-like ceramic reactor. *Process Biochemistry.* 38. 1545-1551.

In: Bacteria in Environmental Biotechnology   ISBN 978-1-61728-350-5
Editor: W. A. Ahmad et al.   © 2011 Nova Science Publishers, Inc.

Chapter 8

INTERACTION BETWEEN ACINETOBACTER *HAEMOLYTICUS* AND CR(VI): THE XAFS PERSPECTIVE

Quek Hsiao Pei, Wan Azlina Ahmad and Shafinaz Shahir

ABSTRACT

Several types of microorganisms have been reported to reduce Cr(VI) to the less toxic Cr(III) via enzymatic reactions. The main purpose of this chapter is to determine the reduction of Cr(VI) by a locally isolated bacterium, *Acinetobacter haemolyticus* (*A. haemolyticus*) using the X-ray absorption fine structure (XAFS) spectroscopy. XAFS analysis consisted of both the X-ray absorption near-edge structure (XANES) and extended X-ray absorption fine structure (EXAFS) spectra. XANES spectra of the rinsed Cr(VI)-laden *A. haemolyticus* biomass indicated that chromium was only present in the form of Cr (III). The nearest atoms coordinated to Cr(III) were oxygens in an octahedral geometry. The longer Cr - O bond lengths (~1.97 Å) obtained from the EXAFS spectra corroborated the presence of chromium as Cr(III) bonded to oxygen. These findings demonstrate the ability of *A. haemolyticus* to reduce Cr(VI) to Cr(III) that was bound to oxygen atoms of the ligands in *A. haemolyticus*.

INTRODUCTION

Recently, a synchrotron-based XAFS technique has provided means for studying biological systems. XAFS offer direct information of metal speciation immobilized in the biomass (Parsons et al., 2002). XAFS is a direct and non-destructive technique to determine the oxidation state of chromium in solids with a detection limit for chromium oxidation states in solids in the parts per million (mg L^{-1}) range. XAFS spectroscopy has the ability to determine atom types and numbers in the near vicinity of the atom whose absorption spectrum is being measured, as well as the distance of these atoms from the absorber. The main advantages of XAFS that make it one of the few structural methods applicable to natural and hydrated samples are as follows: the technique has elemental selectivity by tuning to the absorption edge of interest; no long-range (crystalline) order in the sample is required; and measurements are performed on the "as prepared" samples (i.e., no drying or ultrahigh vacuum environment is necessary). The local structural information obtained from those measurements and from spectra of appropriately chosen, well-characterized standards enable identification and quantification of the functional groups responsible for the bacterial surface complexation, thereby providing a rigorous test of the adsorption model (Boyanov et al., 2003).

XAFS consists of two different complimentary techniques: the X-ray absorption near edge spectroscopy (XANES) and extended X-ray absorption fine structure (EXAFS). The XAFS spectra are split into two distinct regions: a near-edge region that includes the fine structure associated with the edge itself, and an extended fine-structure region that consists of the weak oscillatory structure that may persist to as much as 1000 eV above the edge. These two regions are referred to as the XANES and EXAFS spectra, respectively (Huggins et al., 1999). The EXAFS is the fine structure in the x-ray absorption coefficient starting somewhat past an absorption edge and extending typically 1000 eV further. Fine structure also exists nearer the absorption edge, but because the interaction of the ejected photoelectron with the potential of the surrounding atoms is still strong in this region, the simplifying single-scattering assumption leading to EXAFS cannot be made (Koningsberger and Prins, 1988). The absorption edge corresponds to an x-ray photon having enough energy to just free a bound electron in the atom. When the electrons are in the most tightly bound $n = 1$ shell, the edge is called the K-edge. For the next most tightly bound shell of atoms, the n = 2 shell, the corresponding edges are called the L-edges. At present, these edges are the only ones used to observe EXAFS, though in principle, $n = 3$ or higher shells could be used. X-ray absorption in the photon range up to 40 keV, the range of most importance for EXAFS, is dominated by photoelectron absorption where the photon is completely absorbed, transferring its energy to excite a photoelectron and leaving behind a core hole in the atom (Koningsberger and Prins, 1988). The XANES is an absorption spectrum that covers the range between the threshold and the point at which the EXAFS begins. This is admittedly a rather loosely defined spectral range, its limits being in principle different for each system. Figure 8.1 shows some experimental data in which the different character of the two spectral regimes can clearly be appreciated (Koningsberger and Prins, 1988).

In the XANES regime, multiple scattering of the excited electron confers sensitivity to the details of the spatial arrangement of atoms neighbouring the absorbing one. The details include their radial distance, orientations relative to one another, bond angles, and so on. Changes in the charge distribution around a given atom in different chemical environments can alter core-level binding energies and thus produce absorption edge shifts that show up in the XANES. A practical point worth noting is that XANES structures are usually much stronger than the EXAFS oscillations (Koningsberger and Prins, 1988). Generally, the XANES spectrum is used as a "fingerprint" to identify the form or forms of the element in the material under investigation, whereas the EXAFS region can be mathematically manipulated to yield a "radial structure function" (RSF) from which the local structure around the absorbing element may be inferred (Huggins et al., 1999).

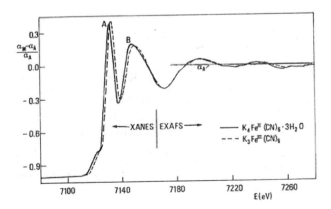

Figure 8.1. K-edge absorption spectra of iron in $K_3Fe(CN)_6$ and $K_4Fe(CN)_6$.

X-ray absorption of fine structure (XAFS) spectroscopy was used to investigate the final oxidation state of chromium and the local coordination of chromium in *Acinetobacter haemolyticus (A. haemolyticus)*. The X-ray absorption of near-edge structure (XANES) spectra provided information on the oxidation state of chromium in *A. haemolyticus* during the reduction of Cr(VI), whereas the extended X-ray absorption of fine structure (EXAFS) spectra provides information on the coordination environment such as the nearest neighbouring atoms.

CR(VI) REDUCTASE TEST FROM CRUDE CELL-FREE EXTRACT (CHANGE R IN CR TO SMALL R)

A. haemolyticus was isolated from the Cr(VI)-containing wastewater from a batek (textile-related) manufacturing premise in Kota Bharu, Kelantan, Malaysia. *A. haemolyticus* was cultivated in NB (8 g L^{-1}, Merck) at 200 rpm and 30 °C (Certomat, B. Braun). It was identified via the 16S rRNA gene-sequencing analysis carried out by First BASE Laboratories Sdn. Bhd., Malaysia, where a 99.5% similarity with *Acinetobacter haemolyticus* (AY586400 and X81662) was obtained from the nucleotide sequence of 597 bp. The nucleotide suquence was deposited to GenBank, where it was given the accession number EF369508. The crude CFE was prepared based on the methods by Thacker et al. (2006, 2007). Mid-exponential phase culture in 200 mL Luria bertani (LB) broth was harvested by centrifugation at 6000 g for 20 mins at 4 °C, washed twice with 20 mL of 10 mM Tris - HCl buffer, pH 7.2 and resuspended in 30 mL of the same buffer. Cells were disrupted by sonication (VibraCell, Sonic and Materials Inc.) for 20 mins in cold condition. The resultant homogenate was centrifuged at 8000 g for 30 mins at 4 °C, where the supernatant (CFE) was used for chromate reductase assay. Protein estimation was carried out using the method suggested by Lowry et al. (1951). Supernatant obtained after harvesting of the cells was also filter sterilized and used for chromate reductase assay. The methods by McLean and Beveridge (2001) and Pal and Paul (2004) were adopted in the Cr(VI) reductase assays. Cr(VI) reduction assays using the crude CFE or supernatant (10 mL) were conducted at 30 °C, with agitation at 120 rpm in Erlenmeyer flasks containing 5 mg Cr(VI) L^{-1} under aerobic condition. One set of LB broth only and autoclaved crude CFE acted as controls. Each treatment was carried out in duplicate, and samples were collected at regular time intervals for 8 h. All samples were immersed in hot-water bath at about 80 ˚C for 1 h immediately after collection to stop the reactions. Cr(VI) was determined according to the standard method described by Thacker et al. (2006).

The specific activity for crude CFE of *A. haemolyticus* was 0.52 μg Cr(VI) reduced mg of protein^{-1} h^{-1} at pH 7.2 and 37 °C. Control sets consist of LB broth and autoclaved crude CFE. The percentage of Cr(VI) reduction with time for both the supernatants and crude CFE (relative to LB broth and autoclaved crude CFE) is shown in Table 8.1. Crude CFE of *A. haemolyticus* was able to reduce 64% of 5 mg Cr(VI) L^{-1} after 8 h of incubation at aerobic condition. The autoclaved crude CFE and the bacterial growth supernatant showed negligible Cr(VI) reductase activity, implying that the Cr(VI) reductase activity is not associated extracellularly but with the soluble fraction of the cells; hence, the enzyme responsible could be either cytoplasmic or periplasmic based (Thacker et al. 2006; McLean and Beveridge, 2001). The specific activity of the cell fractions in other Cr(VI)-reducing bacteria is shown in Table 8.2.

Table 8.1. Percentage reduction of 5 mg Cr(VI) L^{-1} in supernatant and crude CFE of *A. haemolyticus*

Hour	% Cr(VI) reduction	
	Supernatant	Crude CFE
0	0	11
4	0	45
8	0	64

Table 8.2. Specific activity of cell fractions in Cr(VI)-reducing bacteria

Bacterium	Fraction	Condition (pH, ° C)	Specific activity (μg Cr(VI) reduced mg of protein^{-1} h^{-1})	Reference
Brucella sp.	CFE	7.2, 37	0.052	Thacker et al. 2007.
Providencia sp.	CFE	7.2, 37	3.68	Thacker et al. 2006.
Pseudomonad (CRB5)	Crude soluble	Not stated	980	McLean and Beveridge 2001.
A. haemolyticus	CFE	7.2 , 37	0.52	This study

Aerobic Cr(VI) reduction is commonly associated with soluble chromate reductases that use external electron donors such as NADH, NADPH or lactate (Cervantes and Campos – García, 2007). NADH, which can also act as cofactors, was also reported to increase the Cr(VI) reduction activity by CFE for a number of bacterium such as *Providencia* sp. (Thacker et al. 2006), *Pseudomonas ambigua* G - 1 (Suzuki et al. 1992), and *E. coli* ATCC 33456 (Shen and Wang, 1993). However, some strain such as *Cellulomonas* sp. ES6 showed Cr(VI) reduction ability without external electron donors, suggesting its capability to use endogenous electron donors for Cr(VI) reduction (Viamajala et al. 2007). Since the CFE of *A. haemolyticus* also showed substantial Cr(VI) reduction without the addition of external electron donors, it is suggested that *A. haemolyticus* can also use endogenous electron donors for Cr(VI) reduction.

FTIR

Infrared spectra for *A. haemolyticus* cells grown in LB broth added with (30, 60 and 100 mg Cr(VI) L^{-1}) and without Cr(VI) for 24 h were obtained using a Fourier Transform Infrared Spectrometer (FTIR 1600, Perkin-Elmer). The bacterial cell suspensions were pelleted by centrifugation at 7000 rpm, 4 °C for 30 mins. The supernatant obtained was discarded while the pellet was washed in subsequent changes of 0.85% (v/v) saline and DDI water prior to air-drying at 50 °C for 8 h (Kamnev et al. 1997). The dried pellet was ground with 200 mg of KBr (spectroscopic grade) in a mortar, pressed into 10 mm diameter disks under 6 tonnes of pressure before analyzed with FTIR. The analysis conditions used were 16 scans at a resolution of 4 cm^{-1} measured between 400 and 4000 cm^{-1}.

FTIR spectrum of *A. haemolyticus* grown in LB broth without Cr(VI) suggests the presence of amino, carboxyl, hydroxyl, and sulphonate groups with the following band characteristics; 3400 - 3290 cm^{-1} (broad) represents the - OH and – NH stretching groups, most probably from the glucose and protein structure, respectively, 1540 to 1640 cm^{-1} – primary and secondary amides from the protein-peptide bonds which correspond to - NH bending, 1100 - 1000 cm^{-1} due to the C - O bond, which is the characteristic peak for polysaccharides, 800 - 850 cm^{-1} - sulphonate group on the cell surface (Das and Guha 2007). Phosphate functional groups such as P = O, orthophosphate (PO_4^{3-}), and P - OH have characteristic absorption peaks at 1150, 1100 - 1030, and 1040 - 910 cm^{-1}, respectively.

Table 8.3. FTIR analysis of *A. haemolyticus* grown with and without Cr(VI)

Bands (cm^{-1})				Assignment	Reference
Control	Cells with Cr(VI) ($mg\ L^{-1}$)				
	30	60	100		
3422	3445	3440	3445	Bonded hydroxyl group; primary, secondary amines, amides stretching	Mungasavalli et al. 2007.
1648	1650	1651	1651	C = O chelate stretching	Park et al. 2005.
1240	1242	1241	1241	SO_3 groups	Lameiras et al. 2008.
1088	1089	1088	1088	C - O stretching of COOH	Mungasavalli et al. 2007.

However, the peaks occur around the same position as C - N stretching, which is between 1350 - 1000 cm^{-1} (Mungasavalli et al. 2007). When *A. haemolyticus* was grown in 30, 60 and 100 mg Cr(VI) L^{-1}, changes were observed in the region of 1655 - 750 cm^{-1} and 3450 - 2800 cm^{-1}. These changes indicate the metal-binding process taking place on the surface of the cells with certain functional groups (Bueno et al. 2008) such as amino, carboxyl and hydroxyl groups (Table 8.3). Similar findings were reported for Cr-treating cyanobacteria where significant alteration was observed for the characteristic peaks of COOH group, implying Cr complexation with protein molecules (Pandi et al. 2007; Mungasavalli et al. 2007).

X-RAY ABSORPTION FINE STRUCTURE (XAFS) ANALYSIS

Active culture of *A. haemolyticus*, 10% (v/v) was inoculated into four 2000 mL Erlenmeyer flasks containing 400 mL of LB broth each and incubated at 30 °C and 200 rpm until mid-exponential phase. Then, Cr(VI) from stock solution was added into the flasks to give 60 mg Cr(VI) L^{-1} and incubated for 48 h. At the end of the incubation period, the cultures were pooled and pelleted by centrifugation at 13000 rpm for 5 mins at 4 °C, followed by suspension in minimum volume of deionized water. The cell suspensions were then divided into two sets of Eppendorf tubes. One set of the cell suspensions was rinsed twice with PBS (pH 7.4) (Fluka, Switzerland) solution to remove any unbound chromium from the samples. The bacterial suspensions obtained after rinsing with PBS were centrifuged twice to ensure maximum removal of entrained solutions. Both the samples in Eppendorf tubes were placed in flasks sealed with butyl rubber stoppers and purged with N_2 gas for about 8 h. This step was carried out to free O_2 to gain an anaerobic condition and to dry the homogeneous wet cell suspensions. To preserve the samples prior to analysis, the cell suspensions were placed in air-tight Eppendorf tubes purged with N_2 gas that, in turn, was kept at low temperature (4 °C). For XAFS measurements, bacterial suspensions were loaded directly into a slotted sample holder, sealed with Kapton tape.

Cr K-edge XAFS spectra was collected at the XDD beamline, Singapore Synchrotron Light Source (SSLS), operated at electron energy, 0.7 GeV and beam current of 200 mA. The bacterial suspensions were measured in fluorescence mode at room temperature using a Lytle-type fluorescence detector. The reference Cr metal foil and compounds were measured using transmission mode. The references used were Cr foil, $Cr(NO_3)_3$, $Cr(NO_3)_3(aq)$, CrOOH, Cr-acetate, and $K_2Cr_2O_7$. A channel-cut silicon (111) double-crystal monochromator with an entrance slit of 1 mm was used for all XAFS measurements. Energy calibration was carried out using Cr foil. For adsorption samples, multiple scans were collected and averaged to improve signal-to-noise ratio. Data analysis was carried out using WINXAS 2.3. Background subtractions were performed by applying linear and polynomial fits to pre- and post-edge regions. The spectra were then converted into k space (wave vector space $Å^{-1}$) from E space. The conversion to k space was based on the energy of the photoelectrons ejected from the samples. The EXAFS were extracted after background correction using a spline of seven knots taken between 2.0 $Å^{-1}$ and 12.2 $Å^{-1}$. The spectra were then k^3 weighted and Fourier transformed into R space. The same procedures were applied to the reference samples. The phase shift and backscattering amplitude were theoretically calculated from CrOOH using FEFF6 and s2 was determined to be 0.82 by fitting CrOOH and was fixed during the fit to other spectra. The input files for the FEFF6 fitting were created using the Atoms software and crystallographic data in the literature. The interatomic distances (R), coordination numbers (CN), and Debye-Waller factors (σ^2) on the first coordination shell were obtained by fitting to the first peak in Fourier transform.

The XANES spectra of Cr in *A. haemolyticus* cells, together with the XANES spectra of the reference compounds of Cr metal foil, Cr-acetate, $Cr(NO_3)_3$, $Cr(NO_3)_3(aq)$ and $K_2Cr_2O_7$ are shown in Figure 8.2.

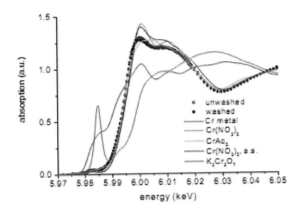

Figure 8.2. XANES spectra at Cr K-edge in unwashed (○) and washed (●) *A. haemolyticus* cells, Cr foil (—), $Cr(NO_3)_3$ (—),$Cr(NO_3)_3$(aq) (—), Cr-acetate (—), and $K_2Cr_2O_7$ (—) standards.

The XANES data for Cr(VI) reference, $K_2Cr_2O_7$ shows a well-defined Cr(VI) pre-edge peak at 5.984 keV (Park et al., 2008) (Figure 8.2). The pre-edge peak is attributed to the electron transition from Cr 1s orbital to 3d (Peterson et al., 1997). The lack of the pre-edge feature for any of the other reference compounds indicates that the Cr was in its reduced valence state, Cr(III). As seen in the XANES spectra, various Cr reference compounds with different oxidation states are distinguishable from each other. The small pre-edge feature for Cr(III) compounds is indicative of Cr(III) bound to oxygen ligands in an octahedral arrangement of atoms. As reported in Peterson et al. (a1997), the pre-edge features are present for octahedral Cr(III) at 5990.5 and 5993.5 eV due to 1s to 3d (t_{2g}) and 1s to 3d (e_g) electronic transitions, respectively.

The results presented in Figure 8.2 indicate that the XANES spectra of the bacterial biomass were identical to that of the Cr(III) reference compounds and the absence of a well-defined pre-edge peak at 5.984 keV, and the chemical shift demonstrates that only octahedral-coordinated Cr(III) existed in the *A. haemolyticus* cells. Both bacterial biomass (washed and unwashed) showed no evidence of an absorption peak for Cr(VI) from the starting $K_2Cr_2O_7$ result in the growth medium. The Cr in the bacterial biomass also did not correlate to the spectrum of Cr metal foil. They are similar to Cr-acetate. Based on the results obtained, XANES was successfully employed to determine the oxidation state of Cr in *A. haemolyticus* cells after growth in LB broth supplemented with 60 mg L^{-1} of Cr(VI). The reduction in the oxidation state of

Cr(VI) reacted with biomass has been previously observed in the Cr K - edge XANES for a number of different biomaterials such as hops (Parsons et al., 2002), native microbial community (Oliver et al., 2003), saltbush (*Atriplex canescens*) (Sawalha et al., 2004), and brown seaweed (*Ecklonia*) (Park et al., 2008). Interestingly, the washed and unwashed *A. haemolyticus* biomass appeared to be similar and, thus, reflected the strong adsorption / absorption of Cr onto the cell surface or intracellularly despite washes with PBS buffer, which served to strip any adventitiously bound Cr ions.

The pre-edge of the biomass and reference compounds in Figure 8.2 was enlarged as shown in Figure 8.3. The geometry of the complex formed between Cr(III) and bacterial cells can be determined if identical or very similar to that of one of the model compounds.

The spectra of Cr in the *A. haemolyticus* biomass closely matched that of Cr-acetate showing their almost similar molecular geometries. Cr-acetate has multi-nuclear geometry in aqueous solution; the nearest neighbors for Cr(III) are 5 oxygen atoms either from acetate (COO⁻) or from water molecules. Cr-O bonds in Cr-acetate have five different lengths. Therefore, the structure may be in an octahedral or pentahedral arrangement. At this local structure, the pre-edge peak shows a slight enhanced intensity compared to the octahedrally coordinated geometry in $Cr(NO_3)_3$ and $Cr(NO_3)_3$ (aq) (Gardea - Torresdey et al., 2002).

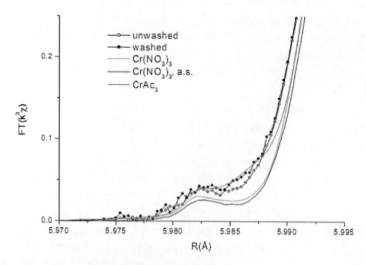

Figure 8.3. Pre-edge spectra of XANES at Cr K-edge in unwashed (○) and washed (●) *A. haemolyticus* cells, $Cr(NO_3)_3$ (—), $Cr(NO_3)_3$(aq) (—), and Cr-acetate (—) standards.

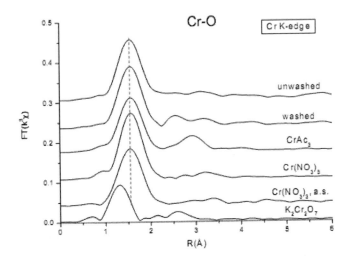

Figure 8.4. Fourier-transform spectra of Cr in unwashed and washed *A. haemolyticus* cells, Cr-acetate, $Cr(NO_3)_3$, $Cr(NO_3)_3$(aq), and $K_2Cr_2O_7$ standards.

The pre-edge spectra of the reference compounds, $Cr(NO_3)_3$ was different from those of the *A. haemolyticus* biomass and Cr-acetate. This implies that the Cr was not bound to the nitrogen atom of amino and nitrile groups (Park et al., 2008). The Cr in $Cr(NO_3)_3.4H_2O$ in aqueous state complexes with H_2O and NO_3 as neighbors to form highly symmetrical complexes. The difference in the spectra indicates that the Cr(III) complexes formed in the biomass are in a non-centro-symmetric geometry.

Figure 8.4 shows the Fourier-transformed EXAFS (FT-EXAFS) spectra of the Cr-reference compounds as well as the *A. haemolyticus* biomass to determine the neighboring atoms of Cr(III) in *A. haemolyticus* biomass. The FT spectra for adsorbed samples show one dominant peak from the Cr-O coordination. The lack of the high-order coordination peaks is an indication that Cr is very dispersive in the samples, similar to an amorphous state for Cr. The FT spectra for the biomass were also almost similar to Cr-acetate, which corroborates the result mentioned earlier that Cr(III) was bound to oxygen ligands (Gardea-Torresdey et al., 2002).

Figure 8.5 demonstrates that the first-shell peak of each sample is satisfactorily fitted. The Cr-O distances were approximately the same (Table 8.4) in the biomass and Cr(III) reference compounds; 1.98 Å for both Cr(III) reference compounds ($Cr(NO_3)_3.4H_2O$ and Cr-acetate) whereas, 1.97 - 1.98 Å for the washed and unwashed biomass.

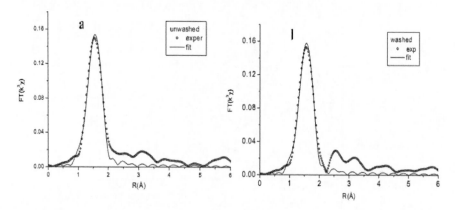

Figure 8.5. One-shell fittings of the Fourier transformation of EXAFS for Cr in (a) unwashed and (b) washed *A. haemolyticus* cells (○) with Cr-O (—).

The longer Cr-O interatomic distance in the biomass than in the $K_2Cr_2O_7$ molecule reveals that the Cr in these samples is in the form of Cr(III). The fact that the oxidation state associated with Cr(VI) is greater than that with Cr(III) results in the shorter first-shell interatomic distance because of the stronger attractive force between Cr(VI) and its neighboring oxygen (Wei et al., 2007). The interatomic distance between Cr(III) and oxygen were reported at 1.96 - 1.99 Å (Park et al., 2008; Parsons et al., 2002; Gardea-Torresdey et al., 2002) whereas for Cr(VI) and oxygen at 1.64-1.67 (Parsons et al., 2002; Sawalha et al., 2004; Wei et al., 2007). Table 8.4 also shows the CN of the Cr(III) bound to the bacterial biomass that is almost similar to that of the reference compounds. In a study using hops biomass, the CN may be determined by the availability or the orientation of the free oxygen ligands on the biomass (Parsons et al., 2002).

The orientation and availability of free oxygen atoms on the biomass may also slightly change the geometry of the complex formed. The CN values support an octahedral coordination of Cr-O in adsorbed samples. However, these Cr-O bonds are dispersive and very different from the perfect octahedral geometry. Their spatial configurations are not as perfect as the octahedral geometry in $Cr(NO_3)_3$. It is, therefore, deduced that Cr-O in the biomass with Cr may be contributed partially from water molecules and ligand groups from the biomass.

The longer interatomic distance of Cr-O in Table 8.4 confirmed the results of the XANES analysis, where only Cr(III) is present in the biomass. In addition to that, the results of the EXAFS fittings for the Cr(III) in the biomass also confirmed the results of the XANES analysis.

Table 8.4. Fitting results in *A. haemolyticus* grown in LB broth with 60 mg L^{-1} of Cr(VI) and reference compounds

Sample	Bond	CN[a]	R(Å)	σ^2(Å^2)
Washed biomass	Cr-O	5.6	1.97	0.0018
Unwashed biomass	Cr-O	6.0	1.98	0.0027
Cr(NO$_3$)$_3$ (aq)	Cr-O	5.7	1.98	0.0024
Cr-acetate	Cr-O	5.4	1.98	0.0030

[a] CN represents the coordination number (number of neighboring atoms), R is the interatomic distances given in angstroms, and σ^2 is the Debye-Waller factor given in angstroms squared.

This analysis proved that the Cr(VI) was not merely sorbed as Cr(VI) in *A. haemolyticus* but rather was reduced to Cr(III).

The fitting results shows that only Cr(III) was present and neighboring with the oxygen ligands. The similarity of the biomass spectra to the Cr-acetate spectra indicates that Cr(III) was bound primarily to oxygen from bacteria rather than oxygen in H$_2$O as in the case of Cr-acetate. Hence, this further suggested that Cr(III) formed complexes more readily with the carboxyl (COO$^-$) group from *A. haemolyticus*. However, the XAFS spectrum taken from one sample would reflect the average local environment of all atoms probed in it (Boyanov et al., 2003). Thus, to be able to separate, identify, and quantify the binding mechanism of Cr in the multiple binding-site case of the biomass requires a clear understanding of the isolated contributions in the spectra from all potential ligands (intra and extracellularly).

CONCLUSION

This study demonstrates that *A. haemolyticus* may be used as a potential agent to decontaminate Cr(VI) contamination in the wastewater system. The Cr(VI) reductase activity was associated with the intracellular soluble fraction of the cells.

ACKNOWLEDGMENT

The authors acknowledge the contributions from the Ministry of Higher Education, Malaysia for the financial support through the FRGS funding and Ministry of Science, Technology and Innovation, Malaysia for the NSF scholarship to Quek Hsiao Pei. Research was carried out (in part) at the Singapore Synschrotron Light Source, National University of Singapore under NUS Core Support C-380-003-003-001, A*STAR/MOE RP 3979908M and A*STAR 12 105 0038 grants.

REFERENCES

Boyanov, M.I., Kelly, S.D., Kemner, K.M., Bunker, B.A., Fein, J.B., and Fowles, D.A. (2003). Adsorption of Cadmium to *Bacillus subtilis* Bacterial Cell Walls: A pH-dependent X-ray Absorption Fine Structure Spectroscopy Study. *Geochimica et Cosmochimica Acta*, 67, 3299–3311. Elsevier.

Bueno, B.Y.M., Torem, M.L., Molina, F., and Mesquita, L.M.S. (2008). Biosorption of Lead(II), Chromium(III) and Copper(II) by *R. opacus*: Equilibrium and Kinetic Studies. *Minerals Engineering*, 21, 65-75. Elsevier.

Cervantes, C., and Campos-Garcia, J. (2007). *Reduction and Efflux of Chromate by Bacteria. Molecular Microbiology of Heavy Metals*. Berlin: Springer-Verlag.

Das, S.K., and Guha, A.K. (2007). Biosorption of Chromium by *Termitomyces clypeatus*. *Colloids and Surfaces B: Biointerfaces*, 60, 46–54. Elsevier.

Gardea-Torresdey, J.L., Dokken, K., Tiemann, K.J., Parsons, J.G., Ramos, J., Pingitore, N.E., and Gamez, G. (2002). Infrared and X-ray Absorption Spectroscopic Studies on the Mechanism of Chromium(III) Binding to Alfalfa Biomass. *Microchemical Journal*, 71, 157-166. Elsevier.

Huggins, F.E., Najih, M., Huffman, G.P. (1999). Direct Speciation of Chromium in Coal Combustion by-products by X-ray Absorption Fine-structure Spectroscopy. *Fuel*, 78, 233–242. Elsevier.

Kamnev, A.A., Ristić, M., Antonyuka, L.P., Chernyshev, A.V., and Ignatov, V.V. (1997). Fourier Transform Infrared Spectroscopic Study of Intact Cells of the Nitrogen-fixing Bacterium *Azospirillum brasdense*. *Journal of Molecular Structure*, 408/409, 201-205. Elsevier.

Koningsberger, D.C., and Prins, R. (1988). *X-ray Absorption: Principles, Applications, Techniques of EXAFS, SEXAFS, and XANES*. United Sates of America: John Wiley and sons, Inc..

Lameiras, S. Quintelas, C., and Tavares, T. (2008). Biosorption of Cr(VI) using a Bacterial Biofilm Supported on Granular Activated Carbon and on Zeolite. *Bioresource Technology*, 99, 801-806. Elsevier.

McLean, J., and Beveridge, T.J. (2001). Chromate Reduction by a Pseudomonad Isolated from a Site Contaminated with Chromated Copper Arsenate. *Applied and Environmental Microbiology*, 67, 1076-1084. American Society for Microbiology

Mungasavalli, D.P., Viraraghavan, T., and Jin, Y.C. (2007). Biosorption of Chromium from Aqueous Solutions by Pretreated *Aspergillus niger*: Batch and Column Studies. *Colloids and Surfaces A: Physicochemical Engineering Aspects*, 301, 214–223. Elsevier.

Oliver, D.S., Brockman, F.J., Bowman, R.S., and Kieft, T.L. (2003). Vadose Zone Processes and Chemical Transport: Microbial Reduction of Hexavalent Chromium under Vadose Zone Conditions. *Journal of Environmental Quality*, 32, 317–324.

Pal, A., and Paul, A. K. (2004). Aerobic Chromate Reduction by Chromium-resistant Bacteria Isolated from Serpentine Soil. *Microbiological Research*. 159, 347-354. Elsevier.

Pandi, M., Shashirekha, V., and Swamy, M. (2007). Bioabsorption of Chromium from Retan Chrome Liquor by Cyanobacteria. Article in press.

Park, D., Yun, Y.S., and Park, J.M. (2005). Studies on Hexavalent Chromium Biosorption by Chemically-Treated Biomass of *Ecklonia* sp.. *Chemosphere*, 60, 1356–1364. Elsevier.

Park, D., Yun, Y., and Park, J.M. (2008). XAS and XPS Studies on Chromium-binding Groups of Biomaterial during Cr(VI) Biosorption. *Journal of Colloid and Interface Science*, 317, 54-61. Elsevier.

Parsons, J.G., Hejazi, M., Tiemann, K.J., Henning, J., and Gardea-Torresdey, J.L. (2002). An XAS Study of the Binding of Copper(II), Zinc(II), Chromium(III) and Chromium(VI) to Hops Biomass. *Microchemical Journal*, 71, 211–219. Elsevier.

Peterson, M., Brown, G.E., Parks, G.A., and Stein, C.L. (1997). Differential Redox and Sorption of Cr(III/VI) on Natural Silicate and Oxide Minerals: EXAFS and XANES Results. *Geochimica et Cosmochimica Acta*, 61, 3399-3412. Elsevier.

Sawalha, M.F., Gardea-Torresdey, J.L., Parsons, J.G., Saupe, G., and Peralta-Videa, J.R. (2005). Special article: Determination of Adsorption and

Speciation of Chromium Species by Saltbush (*Atriplex canescens*) Biomass Using a Combination of XAS and ICP–OES. *Microchemical Journal*, 81, 122–132. Elsevier.

Shen, H., and Wang, Y.T. (1993). Characterization of Enzymatic Reduction of Hexavalent Chromium by *Escherichia coli* ATCC 33456. *Applied and Environmental Microbiology*, 59, 3771-3777. American Society for Microbiology.

Suzuki, T., Miyata, N., Horitsu, H., Kawai, K., Takamizawa, K., Tai, Y., and Okazaki, M. (1992). NAD(P)H-Dependent Chromium(VI) Reductase of *Pseudomonas ambigua* G-1: a Cr(V) Intermediate Is Formed during the Reduction of Cr(VI) to Cr(III). *Journal of Bacteriology*, 174, 5340-5345. American Society for Microbiology.

Thacker, U., Parikh, R., Shouche, Y., and Madamwar, D. (2007). Reduction of Chromate by Cell-free Extract of *Brucella* sp. Isolated from Cr(VI) Contaminated Sites. *Bioresource Technology*, 98, 1541–1547. Elsevier.

Thacker, U., Parikh, R., Shouche, Y., and Madamwar, D. (2006). Hexavalent Chromium Reduction by *Providencia* sp.. *Process Biochemistry*, 41, 1332–1337. Elsevier.

Viamajala, S., Smith, W.A., Sani,R.K., Apel, W.A., Petersen, J.N., Neal, A.L., Roberto, F.F., Newby, D.T., and Peyton, B.M. (2007). Isolation and Characterization of Cr(VI)-Reducing *Cellulomonas* spp. from Subsurface Soils: Implications for Long-term Chromate Reduction. *Bioresource Technology*, 98, 612–622. Elsevier.

Wei, Y., Hsu, L., Wang, H.P., and Chen, K. (2007). XAS Study of Chromium Recoverable from Plating Sludge. *Journal of Electron Spectroscopy and Related Phenomena*, 156–158, 204–207. Elsevier.

In: Bacteria in Environmental Biotechnology   ISBN 978-1-61728-350-5
Editor: W. A. Ahmad et al.   © 2011 Nova Science Publishers, Inc.

Chapter 9

METAL BACTERIA – INTERACTION: CASE OF *THIOBACILLUS FERROOXIDANS* AND AU

Zainul Akmar Zakaria

ABSTRACT

This chapter emphasizes the surface properties of *Thiobacillus ferrooxidans* (a locally isolated Gram negative bacterium from an Au mining environment) and its importance in the binding of Au. Studies conducted were aimed at determining the concentration of metal-binding sites present on the bacterial cells surface, specific bacterial surface area, functional groups responsible for the binding of Au - complexes from solution and elucidation on the mode of Au deposition on/inside the bacterial cells region. From the results obtained, the distribution of Au in *T. ferrooxidans* depends largely on the amount/concentrations of Au present in solution. These conclusions were derived mostly from the surface characterization works carried out. However, possible involvement of other mechanism such as ion-exchange should not be discounted and deserves to be looked into any subsequent studies.

INTRODUCTION

The interaction between metals and microorganisms has resulted in the accumulation of a variety of pollutants, both organic and inorganic, by means of modifying their chemical and/or physical characteristics. It is common knowledge that all microorganisms require some metal-organic complexes in their metabolism; for example, microbial reduction of oxidized metals is important as part of its respiration may depend on the use of the metal as a terminal electron acceptor during energy generation (Eccles, 1999; Volesky, 1990; Mann, 1990). There are various mechanisms suggested for the metal-microorganism interaction such as methylation, chelation, adsorption/absorption, complexation and redox reaction (Mann, 1990). These mechanisms can be divided into two major classifications, namely, the active mode of metal accumulation, i.e., "bioaccumulation," and the rather passive mode of metal uptake from solution which is commonly known as "biosorption" (Volesky, 1990; Ruiz, et al., 1998; Paknikar and Puranik, 1999; Kratochvil and Volesky, 2000; Chang, et al., 1998).

There are several suggested mechanisms for the deposition of metals on bacterial surfaces: precipitation, intracellular accumulation and redox reactions. Metal precipitation results from the reaction between excreted substances from living bacteria with metallic species present in the solution. One example is the deposition of gold particle inside the cell wall of *Sargassum natans* (Volesky and Kuyucak, 1989). Gold complexes, $AuCl_2^-$ or $AuCl_4^-$ would first binds to the biomass by weak interaction as shown in equation 9.1:

$$C=O: \ldots AuCl_2 \text{ or } C=O: \ldots AuCl_3 + Cl^- \qquad \text{(Equation 9.1)}$$

An intermediate reaction could lead to the decomposition of these gold compounds via the reduction of Au to Au^0 or water may be bound to the biomass with hydrogen bonding (equation 9.2):

$$\begin{array}{c} H^+, OH^- \\ R^2 C = O + AuCl \rightarrow C = OH_2O + Au^0 + NaCl \\ Na^+, Cl^- \end{array} \qquad \text{(Equation 9.2)}$$

The reduction of Au from Au(III) to Au(0) has been observed in the isolated cell walls of *Bacillus subtilis* (Beveridge and Murray, 1976), where the formation of microscopic gold crystals was observed. It is possible that gold is bound to sites on and within the cell wall, and these sites act as nucleation points for the reduction of gold and growth of crystals. Non-living cells are cells that are metabolically inactive, independent of growth and also not subjected to the possible toxic surrounding (Macaskie, 1990). The mode of metal immobilization is rather passive compared to living cells. Passive immobilization occurs when a solubilized metal is chelated by an excreted product of a microbial cell or when a metal binds to cell surface by physicochemical reaction such as adsorption or ion exchange (Volesky and Holan, 1995). Metal complexation by extracellular-binding mechanism occurs when the metal binding substances are produced outside the bacteria or in the cell only to be excreted later. These substances can be chelating agents, such as siderophores, or metal-binding extracellular polymers. In the case of metal immobilization, the productions of these substances occur passively (Brierley, 1990).

Transmission electron microscopy (TEM), coupled with a microanalysis apparatus such as the electron dispersive spectroscope (EDS), can provide a valuable input in determining the distribution of the metal-biomass binding throughout the cell structure. When the objective is to obtain the analytical information about the metal-biomass interactions, FTIR is very helpful, especially taking into consideration the simple sample preparation procedures.

Thiobacillus ferrooxidans (T. ferrooxidans) is an aerobic, gram-negative, non-sporeforming, motile, flaggelated and occurring singly or in pairs (Torma, 1988). The shape of its cells vary from large rods with rounded ends, from 1.6 to 1.7 μm in length and 0.3 to 0.4 μm in diameter, to spheres, ovoids and rods from 0.5 to 0.7 μm in length and 0.3 to 0.4 μm. *T. ferrooxidans* multiplies through two common modes of cell divisioning, constriction and partition. It is a chemolithotrophic bacterium that oxidizes ferrous iron and reduced sulfur compounds to meet the necessary energy requirements for growth. *T. ferrooxidans* is also an autotroph with the ability to use carbon dioxide as the carbon source by either fixation from the atmosphere or the utilization of organic compounds (Rossi, 1990). The microorganism possesses a Calvin reductive pentose phosphate cycle, the phosphoenolpyruvate secondary carboxylation derived from the latter, a nitrogen fixation chain and possibly a hexose monophosphate pathway (Rossi, 1990). It is a mesophile growing in a temperature range from 20 to 40 °C with an optimum value of 30 °C. *T. ferrooxidans* requires nitrogen in the form of ammonium ion and phosphorous in the form of phosphate ion for activity and growth. There is also evidence that *T. ferrooxidans* can also fix N_2 from the atmosphere (Brierley, 1997). Trace elements such as Mg, Cu and Mo are also required by *T. ferrooxidans* at

very low concentrations (Bosecker, 1997). At the turn of the century i.e. year
2000, *T. ferrooxidans* has been recently reclassified to the newly designated
genera *Acidithiobacillus gen. nov.* and renamed to *Acidithiobacillus
ferrooxidans* (Atkinson et al. 2000).

SURFACE BINDING SITES AND SPECIFIC SURFACE AREA OF *T. FERROOXIDANS (FERROOXIDANS – ALL SMALL CAP)*

The concentration of binding sites on the bacterial surface was measured
as a function of pH. A volume (2 mL) of the bacterial cell that corresponds to
0.83 mg cell dry wt. mL^{-1} was diluted to a final volume of 10 mL using
deionized water. Addition of 0.25 M HCl was carried out using a microburette
($\pm$ 0.03 mL) until the pH measures around 1.3. The pH meter was then re-
standardized, followed by titration with 0.25 N NaOH until a pH of around
12.5 was achieved. The same titration procedure was also applied to 0.25 N of
each L-glycine, L-aspartic acid and HCl, which acted as control. All the
titration experiments were carried out in duplicates. Total number of binding
sites present on the bacterial surface was determined from the second
inflection point read from the curve of pH versus the amount of NaOH
added/g cells (Figueira, et al, 2000a).

The specific surface area of the bacterium was determined using the
methylene blue adsorption method (He and Tebo, 1998). A stock solution (1
mM, 0.01 to 0.14 mL) of methylene blue ($C_{16}H_{18}ClN_3S.xH_2O$, 319.86 g mol^{-1})
was added to 0.46 mg dry wt. of the stationary-phase heat-treated (SPHT) and
the stationary-phase (SP) cells suspension each in a 25 mL polyethylene
centrifuge tube. The volume was made up to 20 mL using deionized water.
Final methylene blue concentrations prepared ranged from 0.5 to 7 µM. The
mixture was then shaken at 100 rpm, 30 °C for 4 h, followed by centrifugation
(SIGMA 2K-15, B.Braun) at 8225 rpm, 10 mins and 0 °C to obtain the
supernatant. The filtrate was analyzed for methylene blue at OD_{661}. The
amount of methylene blue adsorped by the SP and SPHT cells was determined
based on the difference between the initial and residual methylene blue
concentrations. A blank experiment consisting of the above components minus
the cells was also carried out to obtain a calibration curve.

The concentration of surface binding sites on the bacterial cells was
determined based on the resulting inflection points off the titration curve
plotted (Table 9.1).

Table 9.1.Values for pK$_1$, pK$_2$ and eq. OH$^-$/ mg of cells dry wt

	pK1	eq. OH$^-$/ mg	pK2	eq. OH$^-$/ mg
0.25N HCl	-	-	-	-
L - glycine	2.35	11.19 x 10^{-6}	9.68	25.28 x 10^{-6}
T. ferrooxidans	1.88 - 2.31	0.86 - 0.93 x 10^{-3}	10.80	0.98 x 10^{-3}
L - aspartic acid	2.09	8.10 x 10^{-6}	8.86	18.58 x 10^{-6}

* pK$_1$ – carboxylic group, pK$_2$ – amino group
** 0.25N HCl, L-glycine, L-aspartic acid – acted as control

The titration experiment was carried out with emphasis on the carboxylate and amino groups present in the amino acid fraction of the bacteria. The dissociation constants for the carboxylate and amino groups ranged between 1.8-2.9 and 8.8-10.8, respectively. From Table 3.1, it was shown that the pK$_1$ values for L - glycine (2.35) and L-aspartic acid (2.09) agreed well with the reference value, i.e., 2.34 and 2.02, respectively (Budavari, et al., 1989). In water, L-aspartic acid is present as the aspartate ion. The lower pK$_1$ value observed for L-aspartic acid is due to the presence of an additional carboxylate group on the aspartate molecule while the glycate ion has only one carboxylate group. Figure 9.1 shows the titration profile for cells of *T. ferrooxidans*.

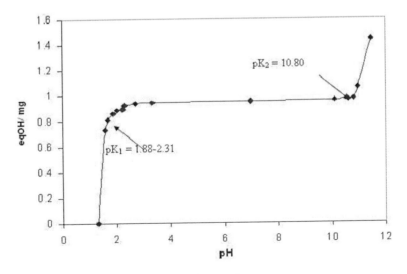

Figure 9.1.Titration profile for cells of *T. ferrooxidans*.

From Figure 9.1, a significant inflection point was not observed at the pK_1 values mentioned earlier but ranged between 1.93 and 2.32. The pK_2 values of 9.68 for L-glycine and 8.86 for L-aspartic acid also corresponds well with the reference values of 9.60 and 8.80, respectively (Budavari, et al., 1989). For *T. ferrooxidans,* the pK_2 value recorded was 10.80. It was also observed that the concentrations of carboxylic group on L-glycine and L-aspartic acid were 11.19 µeq OH^- mg^{-1} and 8.10 µeq OH^- mg^{-1}, respectively. The values were unexpected as L - aspartic acid was predicted to have a higher concentration of carboxylic group based on the extra carboxylate group present. The situation can be explained through the higher amount (in mg) of amino acid salts used for L-aspartic acid (332.8 mg) as opposed to L-glycine (187.68 mg) in preparing both the amino acid solutions (0.25 M). The same explanation can be applied in justifying the high concentrations of carboxylic group found in *T. ferrooxidans* cells with carboxylic group concentrations recorded ranging from 0.86 to 0.93 meq OH^- mg^{-1}.

The role of the amino group in binding metals was studied based on the pK_2 value used. The concentrations of amino groups recorded based on the mg cell dry wt. increased as follows: *T. ferrooxidans* (0.98 meq OH^-), L-aspartic acid (18.58 µeq OH^-) and L-glycine (25.28 µeq OH^-). The low values obtained for *T. ferrooxidans* were due to the use of small amounts of *T. ferrooxidans* cells, i.e., 2.0 mg. For *T. ferrooxidans*, the concentrations of surface binding sites for both the carboxylic and amino groups are almost identical. This could indicate an even distribution of the positively and negatively charged groups on the bacterial surface, due to the acidic pH (2.0) used throughout this work. At neutral pH, the amino and carboxylate groups are present as charged molecules, i.e., NH_3^+ and COO^-, respectively. At very low pH, protonation of COO^- to COOH takes place. Upon addition of OH^-, the amino acids lose two protons, first from the carboxyl group, which has the lower pK value, followed by the amino group, which has the higher pK value. Hence, it can be deduced that during the course of the titration experiment, some of the carboxylic group was deprotonated, which prevented it from having any interaction with the negatively charged Au complexes. Veglio and Beolchini (1997) have reported that two of the more important functional group found in Gram-negative bacterial cell wall are the carboxylic and phosphate groups. The presence of these acidic functional groups is very useful in removing metallic ions and other positively charged metal complexes from solution (Volesky and Holan, 1995). Yee and Fein (2001) have reported the importance of the carboxyl, phosphate, sulphydryl and hydroxyl group in the binding of metals. However, the involvement of these groups in binding negatively charged metal-complexes should not be discounted.

At pH 2.0, the protonated basic amine group would remain in the amino form and act as the primary binding sites for the negatively charged Au complexes (Niu and Volesky, 2000). This is supported by Beveridge and Murray (1980), who stated that the amino groups are not considered as a potent metal chelators unless the metallic ions formed anionic complexes in solution. For example, Pb is charged negatively in its hydroxide complexes; $Pb(OH)_3{}^{4-}$ and $Pb(OH)_4{}^{2-}$. The importance of amine group in binding negatively charged metal complexes is also evident as reported by Volesky and Kuyucak (1989), who stated that in its anionic complexes form, Pb reduced the Au chloride uptake ability of *Sargassum natans* up to 30%. In fact, Cu^{2+} has also been reported to preferentially bind to amines over carboxylate (Beveridge and Murray, 1980). This is reasonable, as Cu has the ability to form cationic $(Cu_2(OH)_2{}^{2+})$ and anionic $(Cu(CO_3)_2{}^{2-}, Cu(OH)_4{}^{2-})$ complexes (Baes, 1976). From the titration experiments, the volumes of 0.25 M NaOH needed to reach an equilibrium condition in the solutions titrated increased as follows: 0.25 N HCl (3.04 mL), *T. ferrooxidans* (6.36 mL), L-glycine (14.16 mL) and L-aspartic acid (22.96 mL). As predicted, 0.25 N HCl, which without the addition of any H-containing moieties, required the smallest volume of OH^- to reach equilibrium condition. The higher volume of NaOH needed to titrate L-aspartic acid compared to L-glycine can be attributed to the release of two H^+ (from the carboxylic group) as opposed to only one H^+ released from L-glycine. For *T. ferrooxidans*, the value recorded was slightly higher than 0.25 N HCl but much lower than both L-glycine and L-aspartic acid.

The methylene blue adsorption method was chosen to determine the surface area of both the SP and SPHT cells. The methylene blue molecule consists of an organic base in combination with an acid. Its structural feature is shown in Figure 9.2.

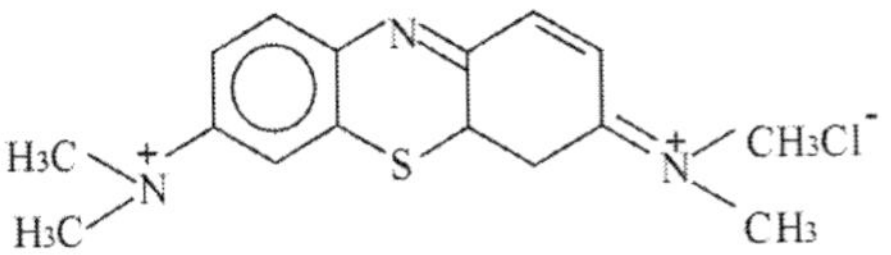

Figure 9.2. Structural feature of a methylene blue molecule.

The molecule measures at 1.7 x 0.76 x 0.325 nm (Taylor, 1985) and in water, exists as monomers at low concentrations ($< \mu M$) or as monomer-dimer at higher concentrations ($\approx \mu M - mM$). In determining the surface area of *T. ferrooxidans* cells, it is assumed that a complete monolayer of methylene blue was formed at the bacterial surface when the adsorption profile reached a plateau. To assess the reaction, the Langmuir adsorption isotherm was applied (Equation 9.3):

$$R = \frac{T_m K C_{eq}}{1 + K C_{eq}} \qquad \text{(Equation 9.3)}$$

where R is the amount of adsorbed methylene blue ($\mu mol\ g^{-1}$), C_{eq} is the concentration of methylene blue at equilibrium ($\mu mol\ L^{-1}$), K is a constant related to the energy of adsorption ($mg\ L^{-1}$) and T_m is the amount of methylene blue needed to form a complete monolayer on the bacterial surface ($\mu mol\ g^{-1}$). The T_m value was then used to determine the bacterial surface area, S (μm^2) according to equation 9.4:

$$S = T_m N_A \sigma \qquad \text{(Equation 9.4)}$$

where N_A is the Avogadro no. (6.02×10^{23} molecules per mol) and σ is total area of methylene blue ($0.55 \times 10^{-18}\ m^2$) when a complete monolayer was formed (He and Tebo, 1998). From the Langmuir adsorption isotherm profiles generated, SPHT cells showed a higher ability to adsorb methylene blue based on the lower residual methylene blue concentration (1.47 to 3.77 μM) compared to the SP cells (1.75 to 5.34 μM). From Equation 9.3, the T_m values for SPHT and SP cells were determined as 0.0249 $\mu mol\ g^{-1}$ (K - 0.212 $mg\ L^{-1}$) and 0.0153 $\mu mol\ g^{-1}$ (K - 0.118$mg\ L^{-1}$). Incorporating the T_m value in equation 9.4 gives a surface area (S) of 0.03371 $m^2\ mg^{-1}$ for the SPHT cells and 0.01311 $m^2\ mg^{-1}$ for the SP cells. These results clearly show that the SPHT acid and heat-treated cells (SPHT) possess a higher surface area compared to the acid-treated cells (SP). Upon heat treatment, *T. ferrooxidans* cells could have a higher surface area-to-volume ratio. From the results obtained, both the SP and SPHT cells showed a good fitting to the Langmuir isotherm with an R^2 value of 0.91 and 0.94, respectively.

FTIR

The FTIR analysis was carried out to assess the main functional groups responsible for the binding of Au by cells of *T. ferrooxidans* (Niu and Volesky, 2000). Au-laden *T. ferrooxidans* cells sample was obtained by contacting 1.0 mg of cells (0.54 mg mL^{-1} dry wt.) with 30 mL of 50 mg L^{-1} Au solution in 250 mL Erlenmeyer flask at pH 2.0. The pH was adjusted using 0.1 M HCl. The mixture was then shaken at 100 rpm for 20 mins at ambient temperature followed by centrifugation at 8225 rpm, 0 °C for 3 mins. Pellet obtained was collected and analyzed for its chemical composition using the FTIR spectrophotometer (Perkin Elmer 1600). Chloroform was used as the solvent, while a blank experiment with deionized water replacing Au solution acted as the control.

FTIR analysis was conducted on the Au-loaded *T. ferrooxidans* cells to identify possible groups involved in the binding of anionic Au complexes with emphasis on the NH- and COO$^-$ group. A summary on the FTIR spectra obtained is shown in Table 9.2:

A significant shift from 3418.8 cm^{-1} to 3288.2 cm^{-1} was observed when *T. ferrooxidans* cells were mixed with Au-chloride complexes compared to the mixing of *T. ferrooxidans* with water. This condition can be attributed to the binding of Au by NH based groups from *T. ferrooxidans* such as amides (RCONH) or the primary and secondary amines (RNH), which is medially detectable between 3050 to 3500 cm^{-1}. The binding of Au that has a high atomic weight would literally reduce the overall vibration of the RNH - Au complex, hence, shifting the stretching vibration to a lower position. An unexpected peak was also observed for CHCl$_3$ at this region, which could be attributed to the presence of water molecules. For the COO$^-$ group (1600 to 1700 cm^{-1}), there was no notable shift upon addition of Au to the *T. ferrooxidans* cells suspension.

Table 9.2. Characteristic peaks obtained for *T. ferrooxidans* cells

Sample	IR bond	
	NH stretching	COO$^-$ asym. Stretching
T. ferrooxidans + water	3414.8 cm^{-1}	1651.7 cm^{-1}
T. ferrooxidans + Au	3288.2 cm^{-1}	1650.6 cm^{-1}
CHCl$_3$	3423.8 cm^{-1}	not detected

This clearly indicates the insignificant role of COO⁻ group from *T. ferrooxidans* during Au binding. Since the experiment was conducted at pH 2.0, complete protonation of the COO⁻ groups would take place, hence, eliminating the possibility of Au binding.

REDUCING POTENTIAL OF *T. FERROOXIDANS* (FERROOXIDANS – CHANGE TO SMALL CAP) TOWARDS AU (CHANGE U IN AU TO A SMALL U)

The cyclic voltammetric method was used to determine the reducing potential of *T. ferrooxidans* cells towards Au. The cells (2.0 mg dry wt.) were mixed with 20 mL of Au solution at pH 2.0 added as $HAuCl_4.2H_2O$ (BDH, 1000 mg L^{-1}) at a final concentration of 150 mg L^{-1}. The mixture was then shaken at 100 rpm for 20 mins followed by centrifugation to obtain the supernatant. The supernatant was analyzed using a voltammeter (Mini and Microelectrode System UM∝E) using the following parameters: scan rate - 4 mV s^{-1}; range measured, 0 to 1500 mV; current sensitivity, 0 to 100 ∝ A; background correction - 0.1 M HCl; purging - N_2 gas; no. of cycle - 1; working electrode-glassy carbon; reference electrode – Ag / AgCl and Pt as the auxiliary electrode.

In this study, Ag/AgCl was used as the reference electrode, while glassy carbon was used as the working electrode due to its inert characteristic. In the presence of an electrical current, the following reactions takes place (Equation 9.4 and 9.5):

$$AuCl_4^- \rightarrow AuCl_2^- + 2e \qquad \text{(Anode)} \qquad \text{(Equation 9.4)}$$

$$H^+ + 2e \rightarrow H_2 \text{ (g)} \qquad \text{(Cathode)} \qquad \text{(Equation 9.5)}$$

Figure 9.3 showed the voltammogram obtained for Au and Au solution in the presence of *T. ferrooxidans* cell, with 0.5 M HCl acting as the background electrolyte. A sharp peak (A) was observed at E_{app} = 1.098 V. This would give an actual E value of 0.876 V after taking into consideration the standard potential of the Ag / AgCl electrode used, 0.222 V (Madigan et al., 1997). This value correlates well with the value suggested for the reduction of Au (III) to Au (I), which was around 0.9 V (Kuyucak and Volesky, 1989). No other peaks were observed in both profiles, ruling out the presence of any inorganic impurities in the solution that resulted from the N_2 purging of the solution.

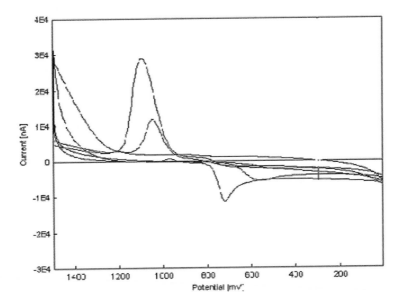

Figure 9.3. Profiles of Au solution in the absence (peaks A and C) and presence (B and D) of *T. ferrooxidans* with 0.5 M HCl as background correction (peak E).

Kuyucak and Volesky (1989) have reported the reduction of 1000 mg L^{-1} of Au (III) to Au (I) upon the supply of an electric current to the Au-chloride solution.

Upon addition of the *T. ferrooxidans* cell, a similar profile (peak B) was obtained for the Au solution with $E_{app.}$ = 1.053 V, which would later give an actual value of 0.831 V. In the presence of *T. ferrooxidans* cell, a decrease in the peak's height was observed, which indicates the dominance of Au (I) species in solution. It was also observed that for the solution containing Au only, the reduction of Au (III) to Au (I) was depicted by a peak recorded at 0.876 V and 26.67 mA (peak A). However, upon addition of *T. ferrooxidans* cells, the peak was slightly shifted to 0.831 V but the height was significantly reduced to around 12 mA (peak B). This clearly indicates the role of *T. ferrooxidans* as a reducing agent for Au, which was probably mediated through the involvement of amino groups from the cell wall. However, the effect from spontaneous Au reduction by UV-irradiation should not be discounted either. No other peak was observed in one flow of electrical current, which could indicate that further reduction of Au (I) to Au (0) had not taken place. Hence, this would suggest that during the experiment, Au was present in its ionic form and not in its colloidal form. Therefore, it can be concluded that HCl as the background electrolyte, did not show any interfering effect on the experiment. Another interesting point to note is when the flow of the electrical current was reversed, both solutions exhibited a significant peak at around 0.7 V (peak C) and 0.5 V (peak D), respectively. The situation is indicative of the reversibility of the Au reduction process. The standard oxidation potential (E^o_{SOP}) for Au (I) to Au (III) is around 0.93 V (Puddephatt, 1978). Both the C and D peaks could be attributed to the oxidation of Au (I) to Au (III).

X-Ray Diffraction (XRD) Analysis

Possible Au deposition on *T. ferrooxidans* cells as Au(0) were determined using the XRD and TEM analysis. The XRD analysis was carried out as follows: 2.0 mg cell dry wt. of *T. ferrooxidans* was mixed with Au solutions at 10, 60 and 80 mg L^{-1}, respectively. The mixtures were then shaken at 100 rpm for 20 mins prior to centrifugation at 8225 rpm, 0 ^{o}C for 5 mins. The obtained cell pellet was then dried in a desiccator followed by placement on an aluminium-based sample holder (10 mm x 12 mm x 2mm). The sample was then flattened using glass slide to allow maximum exposure to the X-rays. Source of radiation used was CuKα ($\lambda = 1.54$ A) with a working cyclic range of between 20 to 80 ^{o}. It was then examined for Au using the X-ray diffraction (XRD) analysis using the Philips PW 1710 - 1830 XRD analyzer.

The investigation on the structural form of Au deposited on *T. ferrooxidans* was carried out using the XRD analysis. Results obtained (diffractograms not shown) did not reveal any peaks showing the presence of organized structured Au particle. This could be indicative of the absence of crystalline Au structure formed on the bacterial surface after the adsorption/ accumulation process. Amongst possible explanations for the situation is the low concentrations of Au used, i.e., 0.05 - 0.36 mM. Most of the reports on the deposition of crystalline structure of Au were reported at higher Au concentrations. Kuyucak and Volesky (1989) reported the presence of distinctive peaks for Au at 38°20', 44°56' and 64°6' while working with the uptake of 1.81 mM of Au by *Sargassum natans*. Lin et al., (2001) also reported the presence of diffracted peaks for Au at 38°99', 44°89', 65°50', 78°30' and 82°47' when Au was present in its nanoparticle form. Sanchez-Loredo, et al. (2001) have reported the formation of Au particle in the aqueous phase at Au concentrations of more than 0.5 mM. During the Au uptake study carried out in this work, Au was present in its $AuCl_4^-$ form i.e., Au(III), which would later dissociate into $AuCl_2^-$, i.e., Au (I) form. At room temperature, Au (I) chloride is metastable, and very slowly disproportionate into Au and Au (III) chloride, Au_2Cl_6 (Puddephatt, 1978). This could support the absence of any Au peak described earlier.

TRANSMISSION ELECTRON MICROSCOPY STUDY

The TEM analysis was carried out for the SP and SPHT cells. Both cells were exposed for 1 and 12 h to 150 mg L^{-1} Au solution (pH 2.0) in a dark environment. Sample preparation for the TEM analysis is as follows: the bacterial cell pellets were first fixed using 3% (v/v) glutaraldehyde for 2 h. It was then washed using 0.1 M phosphate buffer saline (PBS) followed by staining using 1% OsO_4 for 1 h. Distilled water washing was employed before embedding the bacterial pellet in 3% Bacto Agar and left to dry for 30 mins. The embedded cell pellet was then dehydrated using increasing concentrations of alcohol, propylene oxide, a mixture of epoxy resin and propylene oxide (1:1 and 3:1, respectively) and epoxy resin only. It was then polymerized at 37 °C (30 mins) and 60 °C (48 h), respectively. The resultant block was then trimmed accordingly prior to the ultra-thin sectioning procedure (70 to 80 nm thick) using a LKB - IV System 2128 (Bromma, Sweden) ultramicrotome. The sections obtained were then placed onto copper grid (200 mesh) and left to dry at room temperature before stained using 3% (v/v) uranyl acetate (7 mins) and lead nitrate (5 mins). The samples were then viewed using Philips TEM-400 Transmission Electron Microscope.

Upon contacting the cells with 150 mg L^{-1} of Au for 1 h, Au appeared as electron-dense microprecipitates mostly at the cell wall region of the bacterium (Figure 9.4). The microprecipitates have a roughly estimated size of 5 to 20 nm, which was slightly larger than that reported by Vorobyova et al. (2001), i.e., 1.8 - 6.2 nm with a mean particle diameter of 2.5 nm. The deposition of Au on the cell wall region strengthens the notion that Au removal by T. ferrooxidans proceeds via the biosorption route, i.e., passive translocation of metal into/onto the bacterial cells region. This can be attributed mainly to the interaction between the positively charged active groups on the bacterial cell wall (at pH 2.0, i.e., pH of the experiment) such as amines and amides, with the negatively charged Au-chloride ions. The initial Au-chloride ions attached would act as the nucleation sites for more Au-chloride to be adsorped onto/into the bacterial cell wall region. With time, this continuous deposition of Au ions would be translated as electron dense microstructures when viewed under the TEM.

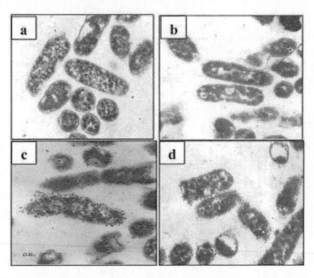

Figure 9.4. TEM micrographs showing (a) SP cells (b) SPHT cells (c) SP cells after exposure to 150 mg L^{-1} of Au for 1 h (d) SPHT cells after exposure to 150 mg L^{-1} of Au after 1 h; bar represents 0.5 μm.

In order to verify the reduction/deposition of Au(III) to its Au(0) state (crystalline-like structure) on the bacterial cells, a method such as the UV-visible spectrophotometry is applicable where a Au absorption band should appear at 525 nm depending on the size of the colloidal particles (Darnall et al., 1986a). The slightly larger Au microprecipitates obtained in this study compared to the one reported by Vorobyova, et al. (2001) was due to the choice of solvent used during the preparation of the Au solution. In this study, Au solution was prepared by adding NaAuCl$_4$.2H$_2$O in deionized water resulting in Au as its tetrachloaurate (III), AuCl$_4^-$ form. However, in the study conducted by Vorobyova, et al. (2001), the Au solution was prepared by dissolving K[Au(CN$_2^-$)] in a mixture of hexane and water. Hexane, which was insoluble in water, could have prevented a complete solubilization of the K[Au(CN$_2^-$)] salts, resulting in a low amount of colloidal Au present in the solution, leading to a smaller particle size observed. Another significant effect from the use of organic solvent in extracting Au from solution is the formation of dense, irregularly shaped nanoparticles of Au during the extraction step where most of the Au was concentrated on the aqueous/organic interface.

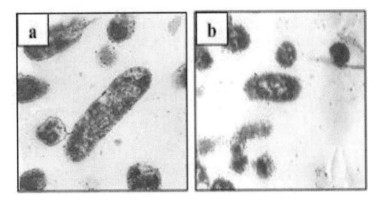

Figure 9.5. TEM micrographs of (a) SP cells and (b) SPHT cells after exposure to 150 mg L^{-1} of Au for 12 h; magnification – 37000 x.

This situation was reported by Sanchez-Loredo, et al., (2001) while using diisobutylketone (DIBK) as the organic solvent. One interesting observation was that prolonged exposure of the SP and SPHT cells to gold for 12 h did not show any significant difference in terms of the amount or size of the Au particles deposited on the bacterial cells (Figures 9.5 a – b).

This situation was somewhat unexpected due to earlier assumptions that upon increasing the cell-Au solution contact time, more Au would be accumulated, hence, increasing the size of the deposited Au particles. A plausible explanation for this situation could be that maximum Au accumulation has been reached during the first hour of cell-Au solution contact time.

CONCLUSION

This study is the first report anywhere on the ability of *T. ferrooxidans* to remove anionic gold complexes from solution. Relatively high Au uptakes suggest the feasibility of using this strain as alternative adsorbent for Au in the industry.

ACKNOWLEDGMENT

The author acknowledges the contributions from the Ministry of Science, Technology and the Environment (MOSTE) for funding of the project via the Top-Down programme (08-01-01-001-BTK/ER/020). Also to PERMINT Minerals (Terengganu) and the Research Management Centre, Universiti Teknologi Malaysia. A special note of thanks to Mr. Megat Radzi Megat Abdul Rahman from the Electron Microscopy Unit, Universiti Kebangsaan Malaysia, Kampus Kuala Lumpur for the excellent works on TEM.

REFERENCES

Atkinson, T., Cairn, S., Cowan, D.A., Danson, M.J., Hough, D.W., Johnson, D.B., Norris, P.R., Raven, N., Robson, R., Robinson, C. and Sharp, R.J. (2000) "A microbiological survey of Montserrat island hydrothermal biotopes." *Extremophiles.* 4, 305-313.

Baes, C.F. (1976) "The Hydrolysis of Cations." John Wiley and Sons, Inc. USA.

Beveridge. T.J. and Murray. R.G.E. (1976) "Uptake and retention of metal by cell walls of *Bacillus subtilis.*" *Journal of Bacteriology.* 1502.

Beveridge. T.J. and Murray. R.G.E. (1980) "Site of Metal Deposition in the Cell Walls of *Bacillus subtilis.*" *Journal of Bacteriology.* 876-887.

Bosecker, K. (1997) "Bioleaching: metal solubilization by microorganisms." FEMS *Microbiology Reviews.* 20. 592-593.

Brierley, C.L. (1990) "Metal Immobilization Using Bacteria" in Ehrlich, H.E. and Brierley, C.L. (eds.). Microbial Mineral Recovery. McGraw-Hill Publishing Company. USA.

Brierley, C.L. (1997) "Application of biotechnology to economic recovery of metals from ores and concentrates." Australian Mineral Foundation.

Budavari, S., O'Neil, M.J., Smith, A. and Heckelman, P.E. (1989) "The Merck Index: An Encyclopedia of Chemicals, Drugs and Biologicals." Merck and Co. Inc. 11th ed. USA.

Darimont, A. and Frenay, J. (1990) "Metals in Aqueous Solution" in Volesky. B. (ed.). Biosorption of Heavy Metals. CRC Press. Boca Raton. Florida. USA.

Darnall, D.W., Greene, B., Henzl, M.T., Hosea, J.M., McPherson, R.A., Sneddon, J. and Alexander, M.D. (1986a) "Selective Recovery of Gold and Other Metal Ions from an Algal Biomass." *Environmental Science and Technology*. 20. 2: 206-208.

Darnall, D.W., Greene, B., Henzl, M.T., Hosea, J.M., McPherson, R.A. and Alexander, M.D. (1986b) "Interaction of Gold (I) and Gold (III) Complexes with Algal Biomass." *Environmental Science and Technology*. 20. 2: 627-632.

Doyle, R.J. (1992) "Cell Walls of Bacteria" ed.: Lederberg, *J. in Encyclopedia of Microbiology*. Vol. 1. Academic Press. Inc.. USA. 479-493.

Figueira, M.M., Volesky, B., Azarian, K. and Ciminelli. V.S.T. (2000a) "Biosorption Column Performance with a Metal Mixture." *Environmental Science and Technology*. Feb.

Grimstone, A.V. (1976) "The Electron Microscope in Biology" in Arnold, E. (ed.) The Institute of Biology's Studies in Biology No. 9. Camelot Press Ltd. Southampton. UK.

He, L.M. and Tebo, B.M. (1998) "Surface Charge Properties of and Cu(II) Adsorption by Spores of the Marine *Bacillus* sp. Strain SG-1." Applied and Environmental Microbiology. *American Society for Microbiology*. 64. 3: 1123-1129.

Kratochvil, D. and Volesky, B. (2000) "Multicomponent Biosorption in Fixed Beds." *Water Research*. 34:12. 3186-3196.

Kuyucak, N. and Volesky, B. (1989) "The Mechanism of Gold Biosorption." *Biorecovery*. 1. 219-235.

Lack, B., Duncan, J. and Nyokong, T. (1999) "Adsorptive Cathodic Stripping Voltammetric Determination of Gold (III) in the Presence of Yeast Mannan." *Analytica Chimica Acta*. 385. 393-399.

Lin, J., Zhou, W., Kumbhar, A., Wiemann, J., Fang, J., Carpenter, E.E. and O'Connor, C.J. (2001) "Gold-coated Iron (Fe@Au) Nanoparticles: Synthesis, Characterization, and Magnetic Field-induced Self-assembly." *Journal of Solid State Chemistry*. 159: 26-31.

Lowry OH, Rosebrough NJ, Farr AL, Randall RJ et al. (1951) Protein measurements with Folin phenol reagents. *J. Biol. Chem*. 193:265-275

Macaskie, L.E. and Dean, A.C.R. (1990) "Metal Sequestering Biochemicals" in Volesky. B. (ed.). Biosorption of Heavy Metals. CRC Press. Boca Raton. Florida. USA.

Madigan, M.T., Martinko, J.M. and Parker, J. (1997) "Brock: Biology of Microorganisms." Prentice-Hall Int'l. USA. 8th ed.. 54-90.

Madigan, M.T., Martinko, J.M. and Parker, J. (1997) "Brock: Biology of Microorganisms." Prentice-Hall Int'l. USA. 8th ed.. 54-90.

Mann, H. (1990) "Biosorption of Heavy Metals by Bacterial Biomass" in Volesky. B. (ed.). Biosorption of Heavy Metals. CRC Press. Boca Raton. Florida. USA.

Mattuschka, B., Straube, G. and Trevors, J.T. (1994) "Silver, Copper, Lead and Zinc Accumulation by *Pseudomonas Stutzeri* AG259 and *Streptomyces Albus*: Electron Microscopy and Energy Dispersive X-ray Studies." *BioMetals.* 7. 210-208

McLean J, Beveridge TJ (2001) Chromate reduction by a Pseudomonad isolated from a site contaminated with chromated copper arsenate. *Appl. Environ. Microb.* 67:1076-1084

Niu, H. and Volesky, B. (2000) "Gold-cyanide Biosorption with L-Cysteine." *Journal of Chemical Technology and Biotechnology.* 75. 436-442.

Paknikar, K.M. and Puranik, P.R. (1999) "Influence of co-cations on Biosorption of Lead and Zinc – A Comparative Evaluation in Binary and Multimetal Systems." *Bioresource Technology.* 70. 269-276.

Puddephatt, R.J. (1978) "The Chemistry of Gold." Elsevier Scientific Publishing Company. Amsterdam. Holland.

Ramli Hitam (1996) "Teknik Spektroskopi Inframerah." Fakulti Sains. UTM.

Ranas, A.G. (1995) "Biological and Biotechnological Waste Management in Material Processing." *Journal of the Mineral Metals and Materials Society.* 47:2. UK.

Remacle, J. (1990) "The Cell Wall and Metal Binding" in Volesky. B. (ed.). Biosorption of Heavy Metals. CRC Press. Boca Raton. Florida. USA.

Rossi, G. (1991) "Biohydrometallurgy." McGraw-Hill Book Company GmbH. 67-74.

Ruiz, M. A., Magana, P.I., Lopez, A. and Guzman, R. (1998) "Biosorption of Zn by *Thiobacillus ferrooxidans.*" Bioprocess Engineering. Springer-Verlag. 18. 539-542.

Ruiz, M. A., Magana, P.I., Lopez, V. and Guzman, R. (1997) "Biosorption of Cu by *Thiobacillus ferrooxidans.*" Bioprocess Engineering. 18: 113-118.

Sanchez-Loredo, M.G., Cabrera-Robledo, A. and Grote, M. (2001) "Preparation of Gold Powders by Means of Redox-active Extractive Systems." *Materials Chemistry and Physics.* 9257. 1-6.

Schiewer, S. and Volesky, B. (1995) "Modeling of the Proton-Metal Ion-Exchange in Biosorption." *Environmental Science and Technology.* 29: 3049-3058.

Tampion, J. and Tampion, M.D. (1987) "Immobilized cells: principles and applications." Cambridge University Press. London. UK.

Taylor, R.K. (1985) "Cation Exchange in Clays and Mudrocks by Methylene Blue." *Journal of Chemical Technology and Biotechnology*. 35A: 195-207.

Torma, A.E. (1988) "Leaching of Metals" in Rehm. H.J. and Reed. G. (eds.). Biotechnology. VCH mbH. Germany. 368-388.

Veglio, F. and Beolchini, F. (1997) "Removal of Metals by Biosorption: A Review." Hydrometallurgy. Elsevier Science Ltd.. 44: 301-316.

Volesky, B. (1990) "Biosorption of Heavy Metals." Boca Raton. Florida: CRC Press.

Volesky, B. and Holan, Z.R. (1995) "Biosorption of Heavy Metals." *Biotechnology Progress*. 11: 235-250.

Volesky, B. and Kuyucak, N. (1989) "The Elution of Gold Sequestered on a Natural Biosorbent." *Biorecovery Academic Publishers*. 1: 205-218.

Vorobyova, S.A., Sobal, N.S. and Lesnikovich, A.I. (2001) "Colloidal Gold, Prepared by Interphase Reduction." Colloids and Surfaces *A Physicochemical and Engineering Aspects*. 176. 273-277.

Yee, N. and Fein, J. (2001) "Cd Adsorption Onto Bacterial Surfaces: A Universal Adsorption Edge?" *Geochimica et Cosmochimica Acta*. 65. 13: 2037-2042.

LIST OF CONTRIBUTORS

Firdausi Razali; Department of Bioprocess Engineering, Faculty of Chemical Engineering and Natural Resources Engineering, Universiti Teknologi Malaysia, 81310 Skudai, Johor

Hanisom Abdullah; Department of Biology, Faculty of Science and Technology, Universiti Pendidikan Sultan Idris, 35900 Tanjung Malim, Perak

Lee Jin Kuang; Department of Chemistry, Faculty of Science, Universiti Teknologi Malaysia, 81310 Skudai, Johor

Madihah Md Salleh; Department of Industrial Biology, Faculty of Biosciences and Bioengineering, Universiti Teknologi Malaysia, 81310 Skudai, Johor

Mailin Mison; Chemical Engineering Pilot Plant, Universiti Teknologi Malaysia, 81310 Skudai, Johor

Muhammed Suhaimee Abd Manaf, Brackishwater Aquaculture Research Center, Department of Fisheries Malaysia, 81550 Gelang Patah, Johor

Nurzahwani Mohd Nor, Department of Chemistry, Faculty of Science, Universiti Teknologi Malaysia, 81310 Skudai, Johor

Quek Hsiao Pei; Department of Chemistry, Faculty of Science, Universiti Teknologi Malaysia, 81310 Skudai, Johor

Roslindawati Haron; Department of Chemical Engineering, Faculty of Chemical Engineering and Natural Resources Engineering, Universiti Teknologi Malaysia, 81310 Skudai, Johor

Rozidaini Mohd Ghazi; Faculty of Agro Industry and Natural Resources, Universiti Malaysia Kelantan, Locked Bag 36, 16100 Pengkalan Chepa, Kelantan

Sabri Sethpa; Chemical Engineering Pilot Plant, Universiti Teknologi Malaysia, 81310 Skudai, Johor

Saffiah Abdullah Khir; School of Science, Universiti Tun Hussein Onn, Locked Bag 101, Parit Raja, 86400 Batu Pahat, Johor

Salmijah Surif; Department of Environmental Sciences, Faculty of Science and Technology, Universiti Kebangsaan Malaysia, 43600 Bangi, Selangor

Seet Seow Wei; Department of Chemistry, Faculty of Science, Universiti Teknologi Malaysia, 81310 Skudai, Johor

Shafinaz Shahir; Department of Biological Sciences, Faculty of Biosciences and Bioengineering, Universiti Teknologi Malaysia, 81310 Skudai, Johor

Siti Khairunnisa Yahya; Department of Chemistry, Faculty of Science, Universiti Teknologi Malaysia, 81310 Skudai, Johor

Suzalina Kamaralarifin; Department of Chemistry, Faculty of Science, Universiti Teknologi Malaysia, 81310 Skudai, Johor

Wan Azlina Ahmad; Department of Chemistry, Faculty of Science, Universiti Teknologi Malaysia, 81310 Skudai, Johor

Zainoha Zakaria; Department of Chemistry, Faculty of Science, Universiti Teknologi Malaysia, 81310 Skudai, Johor

Zainul Akmar Zakaria; Office of the Deputy Vice Chancellor (R&I), Universiti Teknologi Malaysia, 81310 Skudai, Johor

ABOUT THE EDITORS

Wan Azlina Ahmad, PhD is a Professor at the Department of Chemistry, Faculty of Science, Universiti Teknologi Malaysia Skudai, Johor. She has been involved in R&D since 1989. Besides teaching the undergraduate and postgraduate students on biochemistry and biotechnology, she also enjoys collaborating with the industry in carrying out her research. An alumnus of the Universiti of Malaya, Kuala Lumpur (B.Sc.) and King's College, London (PhD), she always believes in focusing her research outputs towards the betterment of mankind.

Zainoha Zakaria, PhD is an Associate Professor at the Chemistry Department, Faculty of Science, Universiti Teknologi Malaysia Skudai, Johor. She has been involved in crustacean waste utilization and cell immobilization projects for the last 15 years. She is currently involved in promoting waste silage in the production of fish diet for the aquaculture industries.

Zainul Akmar Zakaria, PhD is a researcher at Universiti Teknologi Malaysia Skudai, Johor. He has been with the university since completing his secondary education at the Victoria Institution, Kuala Lumpur in 1993. His main research thrusts include the remediation, recovery and removal of toxic / precious heavy metals from aqueous environments. Apart from contributing articles in local and international publications, he also holds the privilege of reviewing articles submitted to various international journals prior to publication.

ACKNOWLEDGMENTS

The editors acknowledge the contributions from the authors in the publication of this book, especially the researchers in the Biotechnology and Biochemistry Laboratories, Department of Chemistry, Universiti Teknologi Malaysia Skudai throughout the years for their painstaking and honest efforts in constantly producing quality results. Not forgetting our families, whose understanding, support and patience have indirectly contributed towards the completion of this book.A big thank you to Ali Reza Mohd Khasim and Nur 'Aishikin Jamaluddin for their patience and expert assistance during the preparation of the manuscripts.

A special note of thanks to Prof. Ramlan Abd. Aziz and the Research Alliance in Biotechnology, Universiti Teknologi Malaysia for the financial assistance towards the publication of this book.

INDEX